From the Four Corners

A collection of stories from different cultures and traditions

Edited by Mike Royston

www.heinemann.co.uk

✓ Free online support
✓ Useful weblinks
✓ 24 hour online ordering

01865 888080

Heinemann is an imprint of Pearson Education Limited,
a company incorporated in England and Wales, having
its registered office at Edinburgh Gate, Harlow, Essex, CM20 2JE.
Registered company number: 872828.
Heinemann is a registered trademark of Pearson Education Limited

Copyright © 2007 Pearson Education

First published 2007

10 09 08
10 9 8 7 6 5 4 3 2

British Library Cataloguing in Publication Data is available
from the British Library on request.

13-digit ISBN: 978 0 435 13136 4

Copyright notice

Selection, introduction and activities by Mike Royston

In-house team
Publisher: Ben Hulme-Cross
Managing Editor: Melissa Okusanya
Design: Georgia Bushell
Production: Jamie Copping

Typeset by ✸ Tek-Art, Croydon, Surrey
Cover design by Forepoint
Printed in China by CTPS Ltd

Acknowledgements

'Dear Mum, Please Don't Panic' by Allan Frewin Jones, from *Dear Mum, Don't Panic* edited by
Tony Bradman, published by Mammoth, 1995 © 1995 Allan Frewin Jones. Reprinted by
permission of Pollinger Limited and the proprietor; 'One Christmas Eve' by Langston Hughes
from *The Ways of the White Folks*. Reprinted with permission of David Higham Associates
Limited; 'Excuses, Excuses' by Andrew Matthews, from *The Great Sandwich Racket and Other
Stories* by Andrew Matthews, published by Puffin Books, 1992. Copyright © 1990 Andrew
Matthews. Reprinted with permission of Penguin Books; 'Father's Help' from *Malguidi Days* by
R. K. Narayan, published by William Heinemann. Reprinted with permission of the Random
House Group Limited; 'Kid in a Bin' by Robert Carter, from *The Pleasure Within*. Copyright ©
Robert Carter. Reprinted with the kind permission of the author; 'Death of the Boy' by Anthony
Horowitz, from *Myths and Legends* by Anthony Horowitz, published by Kingfisher and
reproduced by permission of the author c/o The Maggie Noach Literary Agency; 'The Old
Woman Who Lived In A Cola Can' by Bernard Ashley from *Puffin Post* 1984. © Bernard Ashley.
Reprinted with the kind permission of Bernard Ashley; 'Sharlo's Strange Bargain' by Ralph
Prince, from *The Jewels of the Sun*, 1979; 'The Ghost Train' copyright © 1972 by Sydney J
Bounds; first published in the fourth Armada Ghost Book, published by Mary Danby. Reprinted
by permission of the author and the Cosmos Literary Agency; 'Polyphemus the Cyclops' by
Barbara Leonie Picard, from *The Odyssey*, published by OUP 2001. © Barbara Leonie Picard
1952. Reprinted with permission of Oxford University Press UK; 'Chicken' by Mary Hoffman,
from *Dare You* edited by Wendy Cooling. Copyright © Mary Hoffman. Reproduced by
permission of the author c/o Rogers, Coleridge & White Ltd, 20 Powis Mews, London W11 1JN;
'Poinsettias' by Beverley Naidoo, from *Global Tales*, edited by Donovan, Hicks and Beverley
Naidoo. Published by The Longman Group. © Beverley Naidoo 1997. Reproduced by
permission of The Agency (London) Ltd; 'The New Boy' by Geddes Thomson. Reprinted with
the kind permission of Lucy Thomson; 'The Fight' by Ruskin Bond from *Winners and Losers* ed
Newton 1984. © Ruskin Bond. Reprinted with the kind permission of the author; 'On The
Bench' by Stephen Potts, from *Family Matters*, edited by Miriam Hodgson, published by
Methuen Children's Books 1997. Copyright © Stephen Potts 1997. Is reproduced by permission
of PFD www.pfd.co.uk on behalf of Stephen Potts; 'She' by Rosa Guy copyright © 1984 by Rosa
Guy from SIXTEEN: SHORT STORIES by Donald R Gallo, ed. Used by permission of Random
House Children's Books, a division of Random House Inc; 'Who's Afraid?' by Philippa Pearce,
from *Who's Afraid and Other Strange Stories*, published by Viking Kestrel 1978. Copyright ©
Philippa Pearce. Reprinted with permission of Laura Cecil Literary Agency; 'A Game of Cards' by
Witi Ihimaera, from *Pounamu, Pounamu*, published by Heinemann New Zealand. Copyright ©
Witi Ihimaera 1976 reprinted with permission of Reed Publishing (NZ) Ltd.

Contents

iv

Introduction for Teachers

This collection combines stories from Britain with stories from other countries, cultures and literary traditions.

Its main purpose is to make multicultural fiction accessible and enjoyable to Key Stage 3 students of all abilities. To this end, stories from the western world (normally the UK) are paired by theme or genre with stories from other parts of the globe. The intention is that one should illuminate the other and help students get their bearings on literature which may otherwise seem alien to their interests and reading experience.

The first eight stories are aimed at students in Year 7; the next six at students in Year 8; and the final five (one story stands alone) at students in Year 9. Their language level reflects this progression. Similarly, the activities at the end of the volume have been written to be appropriate to students as they move up through Key Stage 3. Those on the last eight stories are particularly suitable for students preparing for SATs Reading and Writing papers.

The chart on pages 170–172 makes explicit the links between all activities and the objectives in the current English *Framework*. Support materials for teachers are available on the Harcourt website at www.harcourt.co.uk/literature, from which lesson plans and student resources may be downloaded free of charge.

Mike Royston

Dear Mum, Please Don't Panic
Allan Frewin Jones

Dear Mum,

Please don't panic. I can explain about the mess. Honestly. It wasn't really my fault. Not *really*.

I would have called you in from the garden, but I know you hate being disturbed when you're busy with all those weeds, and I thought I'd be able to manage on my own.

You know how I've been trying to think of something brilliant to go to David's fancy dress party as? Well – I finally came up with a really good idea. Oh, while I'm thinking about it, thanks for making the cake – sorry it got trodden on. Anyway, as I was saying, I had this totally brilliant idea that I could go to David's party as a vampire. I've taken that bit of black material as a cloak. I hope you don't mind. And I'm *not* wearing my brand-new trainers to the party – like you said I shouldn't. I can explain why one of them is superglued to the floor in the bathroom. I was trying to mend the shelf over the sink.

Tell you what, Mum! Why don't you make yourself a nice cup of tea before you read the rest of this? You know you always feel better after a nice cup of tea, don't you? And you deserve it, after all the hard work you've done in the garden.

Are you sitting down now? I hope you are, because there are a couple of things I've got to explain. Like why there is talcum powder all over the carpet in your bedroom. Yes, I know I'm not supposed to go in there, but I did have a good reason this time – and it really was a *very* good idea for me to go to David's as a vampire, wasn't it?

But vampires are all *white*, aren't they? Their faces, I mean? And they've got these long fangs for biting people's throats. I couldn't go to the party as a *normal-*coloured vampire with freckles and without any fangs, could I? If you think about it, I'm sure you'll agree with me once you've calmed down a bit. (Are you drinking your tea now? I hope so.)

Anyway, I thought a couple of your false fingernails would make smashing vampire fangs, only they wouldn't stay in my mouth. Which was when I had this other brilliant idea for kind of *glueing* them in place with chewing-gum. It worked really well! But then I thought I'd look even better if I put a bit of talcum powder on my face to make me look really eerie and ghostly. Those talcum powder boxes have the most *stupid* lids. First of all, it wouldn't come off at all, and then it came off all of a sudden and the stupid talcum powder came out of the stupid tin and went everywhere. (Don't worry about cleaning it up – I'll do it when I get home.)

I thought you might be a bit annoyed about the talcum powder going everywhere, so I went to put my vampire face on in the bathroom, and I *snoze* one of my fangs right out of my mouth. I thought it had gone straight down the plughole in the sink. I couldn't believe it!

Remember when you lost your ring down the sink and you used a straightened-out wire coathanger to hook it out? That's *all* I was trying to do, Mum, honestly. I didn't know that shelf was so flimsy. All I did was lean my hand on it so I could give the coathanger a good push, and it just fell straight off the wall. I hardly *touched* it.

And I did *try* to mend that jar. You know? The one Gran brought back from Spain. The one you keep your make-up stuff in. It's a bit of a silly place to keep it, isn't it? On such a flimsy old shelf? And it's only broken into halves. It's not like it shattered to little pieces.

I wanted to mend it for you, but you told me you always kept the superglue in that locked cupboard. How was I to know you'd moved it? I was after the key to the cupboard. I know you keep lots of spare keys in that old coffee jar on the top shelf over the work-surface in the kitchen. (You didn't know I knew, did you? I've known for *ages*, actually.) I'm afraid *that* was when I trod on the cake. Honestly, Mum, if you didn't keep *hiding* things, that sort of thing wouldn't happen. I *had* to get up onto the work-surface to get the key to the cupboard, didn't I? I didn't know you'd moved the superglue. I didn't find out until afterwards. You might have *told* me. (By the way, it was a really nice cake, Mum, David would have been really pleased.)

That's a *useless* key, Mum. I don't know how it happened. It just broke off in the lock. They shouldn't be allowed to sell keys that just break off in locks, should they? I'm sure you'll manage to get the door open somehow, and I've left the other bit of the key on the sideboard so you can *see* how feeble and pathetic it was.

Still, it was a bit of luck that I found the superglue in the drawer under the work-surface after all. That's a much more sensible place to keep it, if you ask me.

That superglue is supposed to stick anything, isn't it? Well, I think you ought to write and complain to the people who make it, Mum, because it certainly didn't stick that jar, and I put tons of the stuff on it.

And then I couldn't get the coathanger out of the plug hole. I really tried very hard, Mum. I'm sure you'll think of some way of getting it out. You're really clever like that.

And that was when I accidentally stepped on the tube of superglue. Wow! When it finds something that it *does* stick, it really works quickly, doesn't it? It's a good job I had my new trainers on, because if I'd had bare feet I'd still be stuck to the bathroom lino! (The other trainer is OK, by the way.)

I would have cleaned up straight away, Mum, but I'm due at David's party in a quarter of an hour. I knew you wouldn't mind me phoning David's mum to come over and pick me up in the car. After all, you were really busy, and you wouldn't have wanted me to walk all that way on my own, would you? And if you'd seen the mess before I had time to explain properly, you might not have let me go at all.

You'll be pleased to know that I found the lost fang. It hadn't gone down the plughole after all! It must have bounced out of the sink, because it was on the floor all the time. I gave it a good rinse before I put it in my mouth, because I remembered you telling me about all the germs there are on the floor. See, that proves I listen to you, doesn't it?

The doorbell has just rung, Mum. It'll be David's mum come to collect me.

Anyway, I'll be at David's party by the time you read this. If I win a prize for best costume, I promise I'll share it with you.

Your loving son,

Jack.

P.S. David said the party will be finishing at about eight o'clock. Could you drive over about that time and pick me up, please?

One Christmas Eve
Langston Hughes

Standing over the hot stove cooking supper, the coloured maid, Arcie, was very tired. Between meals today, she had cleaned the whole house for the white family she worked for, getting ready for Christmas tomorrow. Now her back ached and her head felt faint from sheer fatigue. Well, she would be off in a little while, if only Missus and her children would come on home to dinner. They were out shopping for more things for the tree which stood all ready, tinsel-hung and lovely in the living-room, waiting for its candles to be lighted.

Arcie wished she could afford a tree for Joe. He's never had one yet, and it's nice to have such things when you're little. Joe was five, going on six. Arcie, looking at the roast in the white folks' oven, wondered how much she could afford to spend tonight on toys. She only got seven dollars a week, and four of that went for her room and the landlady's daily looking after Joe while Arcie was at work.

'Lord, it's more'n a notion rasin' a child,' she thought.

She looked at the clock on the kitchen table. After seven. What made white folks so darned inconsiderate? Why didn't they come on home here to supper? They knew she wanted to get off before all the stores closed. She wouldn't have time to buy Joe nothin' if they didn't hurry. And her landlady probably wanted to go out and shop, too, and not be bothered with little Joe.

'Dog gone it!' Arcie said to herself. 'If I just had my money, I might leave the supper on the stove for 'em. I just got to get to the stores fo' they close.' But she hadn't been paid for the week yet. The Missus had promised to pay her Christmas Eve, a day or so ahead of time.

Arcie heard a door slam and talking and laughter in the front of the house. She went in and saw Missus and her kids shaking snow off their coats.

'Umm-mm! It's swell for Christmas Eve,' one of the kids said to Arcie. 'It's snowin' like the deuce, and mother came near driving through a stop light. Can't hardly see for the snow. It's swell!'

'Supper's ready,' Arcie said. She was thinking how her shoes weren't very good for walking in snow.

It seemed like the white folks took as long as they could to eat that evening. While Arcie was washing dishes, the Missus came out with her money.

'Arcie,' the Missus said, 'I'm so sorry, but would you mind if I just gave you five dollars tonight? The children have made me run short of change, buying presents and all.'

'I'd like to have seven,' Arcie said. 'I needs it.'

'Well, I just haven't got seven,' the Missus said. 'I didn't know you'd want all your money before the end of the week, anyhow. I just haven't got it to spare.'

Arcie took five. Coming out of the hot kitchen, she wrapped up as well as she could and hurried by the house where she roomed to get little Joe. At least he could look at the Christmas trees in the windows downtown.

The landlady, a big light yellow woman, was in a bad humour. She said to Arcie, 'I thought you was comin' home early and get this child. I guess you know I want to go out, too, once in awhile.'

Arcie didn't say anything for, if she had, she knew the landlady would probably throw it up to her that she wasn't getting paid to look after the child both night and day.

'Come on, Joe,' Arcie said to her son, 'Let's us go in the street.'

'I hears they got a Santa Claus down town,' Joe said, wriggling into his worn little coat. 'I wants to see him.'

'Don't know 'bout that,' his mother said, 'but hurry up and get your rubbers on. Stores'll all be closed directly.'

It was six or eight blocks downtown. They trudged along through the falling snow, both of them a little cold. But the snow was pretty!

The main street was hung with bright red and blue lights. In front of the City Hall there was a Christmas tree – but it didn't have no presents on it, only lights. In the store windows there were lots of toys – for sale.

Joe kept saying, 'Mama, I want...'

But mama kept walking ahead. It was nearly ten, when the stores were due to close, and Arcie wanted to get Joe some cheap gloves and something to keep him warm, as well as a toy or two. She thought she might come across a rummage sale where they had children's clothes. And in the ten-cent store, she could get some toys.

'O-oo! Lookee...,' little Joe kept saying, and pointing at things in the windows. How warm and pretty the lights were, and the shops, and the electric signs through the snow.

It took Arcie more than a dollar to get Joe's mittens and things he needed. In the A. & P. Arcie bought a big box of hard candies for 49c. And then she guided Joe through the crowd on the street until they came to the dime store. Near the ten-cent store they passed a moving picture theatre. Joe said he wanted to go in and see the movies.

Arcie said, 'Ump-un! No, child! This ain't Baltimore where they have shows for coloured, too. In these here small towns, they don't let coloured folks in. We can't go in there.'

'Oh,' said little Joe.

In the ten-cent store, there was an awful crowd. Arcie told Joe to stand outside and wait for her. Keeping hold of him in the crowded store would be a job. Besides she didn't want him to see what toys she was buying. They were to be a surprise from Santa Claus tomorrow.

Little Joe stood outside the ten-cent store in the light, and the snow, and people passing. Gee, Christmas was pretty. All tinsel and stars and cotton. And Santa Claus a-coming from somewhere, dropping things in stockings. And all the people in the streets were carrying things, and the kids looked happy.

But Joe soon got tired of just standing and thinking and waiting in front of the ten-cent store. There were so many things to look at in the other windows. He moved along up the block a little, and then a little more, walking and looking. In fact, he moved until he came to the white folks' picture show.

In the lobby of the moving picture show, behind the plate glass doors, it was all warm and glowing and awful pretty. Joe stood looking in, and as he looked his eyes began to make out, in there blazing beneath holly and coloured streamers and the electric stars of the lobby, a marvellous Christmas tree. A group of children and grown-ups, white, of course, were standing around a big jovial man in red beside the tree. Or was it a man? Little Joe's eyes opened wide. No, it was not a man after all. It was Santa Claus!

Little Joe pushed open one of the glass doors and ran into the lobby of the white moving picture show. Little Joe went right through the crowd and up to where he could get a good look at Santa Claus. And Santa Claus was giving away gifts, little presents for children, little boxes of animal crackers and stick-candy canes. And behind him on the tree was a big sign (which little Joe didn't know how to read). It said, to those who understood, MERRY XMAS FROM SANTA CLAUS TO OUR YOUNG PATRONS.

Around the lobby, other signs said, WHEN YOU COME

OUT OF THE SHOW STOP WITH YOUR CHILDREN AND SEE OUR SANTA CLAUS. And another announced, GEM THEATRE MAKES ITS CUSTOMERS HAPPY – SEE OUR SANTA.

And there was Santa Claus in a red suit and a white beard all sprinkled with tinsel snow. Around him were rattles and drums and rocking horses which he was not giving away. But the signs on them said (could little Joe have read) that they would be presented from the stage on Christmas Day to the holders of lucky numbers. Tonight, Santa Claus was only giving away candy, and stick-candy canes, and animal crackers to the kids.

Joe would have liked terribly to have a stick-candy cane. He came a little closer to Santa Claus, until he was right in the front of the crowd. And then Santa Claus saw Joe.

Why is it that lots of white people always grin when they see a Negro child? Santa Claus grinned. Everybody else grinned, too, looking at little black Joe – who had no business in the lobby of a white theatre. Then Santa Claus stooped down and slyly picked up one of his lucky number rattles, a great big loud tin-pan rattle such as they use in cabarets. And he shook it fiercely right at Joe. That was funny. The white people laughed, kids and all. But little Joe didn't laugh. He was scared. To the shaking of the big rattle, he turned and flew out of the warm lobby of the theatre, out into the street where the snow was and the people. Frightened by laughter, he had begun to cry. He went looking for his mama. In his heart he never thought Santa Claus shook great rattles at children like that – and then laughed.

In the crowd on the street he went the wrong way. He couldn't find the ten-cent store or his mother. There were too many people, all white people, moving like white shadows in the snow, a world of white people.

It seemed to Joe an awfully long time till he suddenly saw Arcie, dark and worried-looking, cut across the sidewalk through the passing crowd and grab him. Although her arms were full of packages, she still managed with one free hand to shake him until his teeth rattled.

'Why didn't you stand where I left you?' Arcie demanded loudly. 'Tired as I am, I got to run all over the streets in the night lookin' for you. I'm a great mind to wear you out.'

When little Joe got his breath back, on the way home, he told his mama he had been in the moving picture show.

'But Santa Claus didn't give me nothin',' Joe said tearfully. 'He made a big noise at me and I runned out.'

'Serves you right,' said Arcie, trudging through the snow. 'You had no business in there. I told you to stay where I left you.'

'But I seed Santa Claus in there,' little Joe said, 'so I went in.'

'Huh! That wasn't no Santa Claus,' Arcie explained. 'If it was, he wouldn't a-treated you like that. That's a theatre for white folks – I told you once – and he's just an old white man.'

'Oh…,' said little Joe.

Excuses, Excuses
Andrew Matthews

Not long after the roof blew off Wyvern Copse School, Two Red noticed that there was a battle going on. The battle was between Gerry Atkins and Mr Haggerty, Two Red's French teacher, and it was about homework: or rather, the lack of it.

It was a surprising struggle. Gerry was a pear-shaped boy with brown hair and freckles whose only outstanding quality was his unremarkability; Mr Haggerty was a large man with a mane of white hair, bristling eyebrows and a reputation for prickliness. He was particularly prickly when it came to homework and was Master of the Awkward Question.

'I couldn't do the exercise you set us last night, I didn't understand it, sir,' would be met with, 'Then where is the work you did instead?'

Any pupil honest enough to admit forgetting homework would be given verbs to write out. Mr Haggerty took pains to point out that the verbs were not a punishment but an aid to the memory.

The first time Gerry Atkins failed to do his French, he had a genuine enough excuse – he had been ill when it was set. Mr Haggerty had nodded sympathetically and said that Gerry would have to do a double homework to make up for the time he had lost.

Gerry was aggrieved by this.

'It's not fair!' he complained loudly to his mate, Tim Worcester. 'He's punishing me because I was ill! It wasn't my fault!'

'It was in a way,' said Tim. 'You told me it was all those

Mexican beans you ate.'

'I was hungry!' Gerry countered. 'I like Mexican beans! I didn't know that eating two lots would turn me into a human aerosol can the next day, did I? Now I've got double French homework because of it! That Haggerty bloke isn't human!'

'Of course he isn't,' Tim agreed. 'He's a teacher.'

Gerry set his jaw and squinted determinedly. 'Well, I'm not doing it! He can whistle for his precious homework!'

'But, Gerry!' squeaked Tim. 'It's Mr Haggerty!'

'I know.'

'Winding him up is like juggling with nitro-glycerine! Just do the extra work! A quiet life's better than a noisy, painful death!'

'No!' said Gerry. 'This is a matter of principle!'

Battle was joined in the next French lesson. When Mr Haggerty asked for the books to be handed in, Gerry's hand went up in the air like the tail of a cat who has just heard a tin being opened.

'Ah, Atkins!' smiled Mr Haggerty. 'You're about to give in two homeworks, aren't you?'

'No, sir,' said Gerry. 'I haven't done any homework at all, sir.'

Mr Haggerty's smile stayed fixed but his eyes narrowed. 'Why not, Atkins?'

'We had a power cut last night, sir.'

Power cuts had been frequent since the Great October Storm and it was not the first time that Mr Haggerty had dealt with this particular excuse.

'Didn't you have any candles in your house, Atkins?'

'Yes, sir, a boxful, sir!' responded Gerry.

'Then why didn't you do your homework by candlelight?' concluded Mr Haggerty triumphantly.

'Well, sir,' began Gerry, 'the thing is, the box of candles

was in the garden shed. My mum sent me out to get them. I was bringing them back into the house when I tripped over and they went flying. It was so dark because of the power cut, I couldn't find them, sir!'

If Mr Haggerty had been a dog, he would have growled; as it was he frowned severely and when he spoke, the temperature of his voice was well below zero.

'I'm going to give you the benefit of the doubt, Atkins, and believe you. This time. You will do both homeworks by Friday and show them to me at the start of the lesson.'

'My granny's coming to stay, sir!' said Gerry hurriedly.

Mr Haggerty looked puzzled. 'A fascinating snippet of information, Atkins, whose relevance, for the moment, eludes me!'

'Well, you see, sir, my granny's a bit funny—'

'I don't care if she's an award-winning comedienne, laddie!' roared Mr Haggerty. 'Get those homeworks done or else!'

In registration on Friday morning, Gerry and Tim were approached by Wayne Armitage, Two Red's wheeler-dealer.

'You done that French then, Atko?' he asked confidentially.

'No.'

Wayne whistled.

'You gotta lotta bottle, kid,' he said. 'Either that or you're a complete wally! Anyway, fancy a little flutter?'

'Flutter?' echoed Gerry.

'You know, a bet!' Wayne explained.

'A bet on what?'

'5p stake,' said Wayne. 'Two-to-one, you gets put in detention. Five-to-one, 'Aggerty drags you straight down to the 'Ead!'

'What if he lets me off?' asked Gerry.

Wayne laughed, ''Aggerty let you off? Ten-to-one chance, mate!'

'Right!' said Gerry, digging in his pocket for a five pence piece. 'You're on!'

The atmosphere was tense at the start of French. All eyes were fixed on Gerry as, with a flourish, he set his exercise book down on Mr Haggerty's table. Mr Haggerty leafed through the book and his eyes bulged.

'What's the meaning of this, Atkins?' he rasped. 'Your homework is still not done!'

'I tried to tell you the last time, sir! My granny's staying with us.'

'Atkins,' seethed Mr Haggerty, 'I'm going to ask you a simple question, but I want you to think carefully about your answer, because it could be your last words! What does your grandmother have to do with it?'

'She hates anything to do with France, sir! She suffers from Francophobia.'

'What?' shrieked Mr Haggerty

'Anything to do with France gives her one of her turns, sir,' said Gerry. 'She trampled the remote control on our telly last year when Delia Smith did a recipe for coq au vin. I can't do any French homework while she's in the house, sir.'

Mr Haggerty tried to speak several times, without success. When his voice eventually emerged, it was strangled, as though he were doing to his vocal cords what he would like to do to Gerry.

'Atkins, when is your grandmother leaving?'

'Tonight, sir.'

'Very well. Over the weekend, you'll do the two homeworks you owe me, plus the one I'm setting this lesson. You'll show them to me on Monday. And … Atkins?'

'Sir?'

'If you're taken ill, dictate your homework to a nurse!' snapped Mr Haggerty. 'If the illness proves fatal, dictate it to a medium!'

At the end of the lesson, Wayne Armitage paid Gerry fifty pence. He was grinning broadly as he did it.

'Magic!' he exclaimed admiringly.

'What are you so happy about?' Gerry demanded. 'Does losing money appeal to your sense of humour, or something?'

'Who's losin' money?' beamed Wayne. 'Twenty kids in our class bet that you'd get put in detention! I'm 50p up on the deal! I'm openin' another book for Monday. Two-to-one you do the 'omework, ten-to-one you don't do it and you gets a detention!'

'What if I don't do it and get away with it?' Gerry asked curiously.

'Impossible!' gasped Wayne.

'Like to bet?'

'Bookies never bet!' said Wayne scornfully. 'It's a mug's game!'

In registration on Monday morning, Gerry was the centre of attention.

'I feel quietly confident,' he told Tim. 'I've been in training all over the weekend and I think I'm fully prepared.'

'I couldn't eat this morning!' Tim confessed. 'I kept on thinking what Mr Haggerty was going to do to you. It put me off my breakfast!'

'I had porridge, kippers and toast!' said Gerry nonchalantly. 'I got a couple of Mars bars down on the way to school as well!'

'No point dying on an empty stomach, I suppose!' said Tim.

Gerry smiled enigmatically.

The air in the French room was electric. The spectators took their seats and a buzz of excitement went around as Gerry Atkins, one of the contenders, took his place at the back of the class. The buzz died to an expectant silence as Mr Haggerty entered and the crowd prepared themselves for a no-holds-barred contest.

'Take out your exercise books and turn to your homework!' commanded Mr Haggerty.

In the ensuing shuffle, Gerry's arm lifted into the air. 'Please, sir, may I leave the room, sir!' he whispered desperately.

'No, you may not, Atkins! Too much for you, eh, laddie?' sneered Mr Haggerty. 'Lost the stomach for it? Open that exercise book.'

'But … sir…'

'Do as you're told!' bawled Mr Haggerty.

Gerry opened his French book on the table. 'Sir…' he whimpered.

'It's no use being pathetic!' boomed Mr Haggerty, advancing. 'There's no escape this time, is there, laddie? I've got you right—'

Gerry was sick – gloriously and spectacularly sick – all over his French book.

The next morning, Mr Haggerty sent for Gerry during registration and met him in the French Department Office.

'All right, Atkins!' he sighed. 'You win. I want to call a truce.'

'Sir?' said Gerry innocently.

'We'll forget about the homeworks you owe me, but as of this Friday, you'll do your French like everybody else, or I'll take you to the Headmaster. Is that clear?'

'Yes, sir.'

Mr Haggerty handed over a new exercise book. 'No more excuses, Atkins?'

'No, sir!'

'Right!' smiled Mr Haggerty. 'When you get back to your form base, send Wayne Armitage over to me. I want to collect my winnings.'

'Winnings, sir?' frowned Gerry.

'Yes,' said Mr Haggerty. 'I bet 2p that you'd get away with it yesterday. Wayne offered odds of hundred-to-one. He owes me two pounds.'

Father's Help
R. K. Narayan

Lying in bed, Swami realised with a shudder that it was Monday morning. It looked as though only a moment ago it had been the last period on Friday; already Monday was here. He hoped that an earthquake would reduce the school building to dust, but that good building – Albert Mission School – had withstood similar prayers for over a hundred years now. At nine o'clock Swaminathan wailed, 'I have a headache.' His mother said, 'Why don't you go to school in a *jutka*?'*

'So that I may be completely dead at the other end? Have you any idea what it means to be jolted in a *jutka*?'

'Have you many important lessons today?'

'Important! Bah! That geography teacher has been teaching the same lesson for over a year now. And we have arithmetic, which means for a whole period we are going to be beaten by the teacher … Important lessons!'

And Mother generously suggested that Swami might stay at home.

At 9:30, when he ought to have been shouting in the school prayer hall, Swami was lying on the bench in Mother's room. Father asked him, 'Have you no school today?'

'Headache,' Swami replied.

'Nonsense! Dress up and go.'

'Headache.'

'Loaf about less on Sundays and you will be without a headache on Mondays.'

---

*jutka: a two-wheeled, horse-drawn carriage

Swami knew how stubborn his father could be and changed his tactics. 'I can't go so late to the class.'

'I agree, but you'll have to; it is your own fault. You should have asked me before deciding to stay away.'

'What will the teacher think if I go so late?'

'Tell him you had a headache and so are late.'

'He will beat me if I say so.'

'Will he? Let us see. What is his name?'

'Samuel.'

'Does he beat the boys?'

'He is very violent, especially with boys who come late. Some days ago a boy was made to stay on his knees for a whole period in a corner of the class because he came late, and that after getting six cuts from the cane and having his ears twisted. I wouldn't like to go late to Samuel's class.'

'If he is so violent, why not tell your headmaster about it?'

'They say that even the headmaster is afraid of him. He is such a violent man.'

And then Swami gave a lurid account of Samuel's violence; how when he started caning he would not stop until he saw blood on the boy's hand, which he made the boy press to his forehead like a vermilion marking. Swami hoped that with this his father would be made to see that he couldn't go to his class late. But Father's behaviour took an unexpected turn. He became excited. 'What do these swine mean by beating our children? They must be driven out of service. I will see…'

The result was he proposed to send Swami late to his class as a kind of challenge. He was also going to send a letter with Swami to the headmaster. No amount of protest from Swami was of any avail: Swami had to go to school.

By the time he was ready Father had composed a long letter to the headmaster, put it in an envelope and sealed it.

'What have you written, Father?' Swaminathan asked apprehensively.

'Nothing for you. Give it to your headmaster and go to your class.'

'Have you written anything about our teacher Samuel?'

'Plenty of things about him. When your headmaster reads it he will probably dismiss Samuel from the school and hand him over to the police.'

'What has he done, Father?'

'Well there is a full account of everything he has done in the letter. Give it to your headmaster and go to your class. You must bring an acknowledgement from him in the evening.'

Swami went to school feeling that he was the worst perjurer* on earth. His conscience bothered him: he wasn't at all sure if he had been accurate in his description of Samuel. He could not decide how much of what he said was imagined and how much of it was real. He stopped for a moment on the roadside to make up his mind about Samuel: he was not such a bad man after all. Personally he was much more genial than the rest; often he cracked a joke or two centring around Swami's inactions, and Swami took it as a mark of Samuel's personal regard for him. But there was no doubt that he treated people badly... His cane skinned people's hands. Swami cast his mind about for an instance of this. There was none within his knowledge. Years and years ago he was reputed to have skinned the knuckles of a boy in First Standard and made him smear the blood on his face. No one had actually seen it. But year after year the story

---

perjurer: liar

persisted among the boys ... Swami's head was dizzy with confusion in regard to Samuel's character – whether he was good or bad, whether he deserved the allegations in the letter or not ... Swami felt an impulse to run home and beg his father to take back the letter. But Father was an obstinate man.

As he approached the yellow building he realised that he was perjuring himself and was ruining his teacher. Probably the headmaster would dismiss Samuel and then the police would chain him and put him in jail. For all this disgrace, humiliation and suffering, who would be responsible? Swami shuddered. The more he thought of Samuel, the more he grieved for him – the dark face, his small red-streaked eyes, his thin line of moustache, his unshaven cheek and chin, his yellow coat; everything filled Swami with sorrow. As he felt the bulge of the letter in his pocket, he felt like an executioner. For a moment he was angry with his father and wondered why he should not fling into the gutter the letter of a man so unreasonable and stubborn.

As he entered the school gate an idea occurred to him, a sort of solution. He wouldn't deliver the letter to the headmaster immediately, but at the end of the day – to that extent he would disobey his father and exercise his independence. There was nothing wrong in it, and Father would not know it anyway. If the letter was given at the end of the day there was a chance that Samuel might do something to justify the letter.

Swami stood at the entrance to his class. Samuel was teaching arithmetic. He looked at Swami for a moment. Swami stood hoping that Samuel would fall on him and tear his skin off. But Samuel merely asked, 'Are you just coming to the class?'

'Yes, sir.'

'You are half an hour late.'

'I know it.' Swami hoped that he would be attacked now. He almost prayed: 'God of Thirupathi, please make Samuel beat me.'

'Why are you late?'

Swami wanted to reply, 'Just to see what you can do.' But he merely said, 'I have a headache, sir.'

'Then why did you come to the school at all?'

A most unexpected question from Samuel. 'My father said that I shouldn't miss the class, sir,' said Swami.

This seemed to impress Samuel. 'Your father is quite right; a very sensible man. We want more parents like him.'

'Oh, you poor worm!' Swami thought. 'You don't know what my father has done to you.' He was more puzzled that ever about Samuel's character.

'All right, go to your seat. Have you still a headache?'

'Slightly, sir.'

Swami went to his seat with a bleeding heart. He had never met a man so good as Samuel. The teacher was inspecting the home lessons, which usually produced (at least, according to Swami's impression) scenes of great violence. Notebooks would be flung at faces, boys would be abused, caned and made to stand up on benches. But today Samuel appeared to have developed more tolerance and gentleness. He pushed away the bad books, just touched people with the cane, never made anyone stand up for more than a few minutes. Swami's turn came. He almost thanked God for the chance.

'Swaminathan, where is your homework?'

'I have not done any homework, sir,' he said blandly.

There was a pause.

'Why – headache?' asked Samuel.

'Yes, sir.'

'All right, sit down.' Swami sat down, wondering what had come over Samuel. The period came to an end and Swami felt desolate. The last period of the day was again taken by Samuel. He came this time to teach them Indian history. The period began at 3:45 and ended at 4:30. Swaminathan had sat through the previous periods thinking acutely. He could not devise any means of provoking Samuel. When the clock struck four Swami felt desperate. Half an hour more. Swami was reading the red text, the portion describing Vasco da Gama's arrival in India. The boys listened in half-languor. Swami suddenly asked at the top of his voice, 'Why did not Columbus come to India, sir?'

'He lost his way.'

'I can't believe it; it is unbelievable, sir.'

'Why?'

'Such a great man. Would he have not known the way?'

'Don't shout. I can hear you quite well.'

'I am not shouting, sir; this is my ordinary voice, which God has given me. How can I help it?'

'Shut up and sit down.'

Swaminathan sat down, feeling slightly happy at his success. The teacher threw a puzzled, suspicious glance at him and resumed his lessons.

His next chance occurred when Sankar of the first bench got up and asked, 'Sir, was Vasco da Gama the very first person to come to India?'

Before the teacher could answer, Swami shouted from the back bench, 'That's what they say.'

The teacher and all the boys looked at Swami. The teacher was puzzled by Swami's obtrusive behaviour today. 'Swaminathan, you are shouting again.'

'I am not shouting, sir. How can I help my voice, given by God?'

The school clock struck a quarter-hour. A quarter more. Swami felt he must do something drastic in fifteen minutes. Samuel had no doubt scowled at him and snubbed him, but it was hardly adequate. Swami felt that with a little more effort Samuel could be made to deserve dismissal and imprisonment.

The teacher came to the end of a section in the textbook and stopped. He proposed to spend the remaining few minutes putting questions to the boys. He ordered the whole class to put away their books, and asked someone in the second row, 'What is the date of Vasco da Gama's arrival in India?'

Swaminathan shot up and screeched, '1648, December 20.'

'You needn't shout,' said the teacher. He asked, 'Has your headache made you mad?'

'I have no headache now, sir,' replied the thunderer brightly.

'Sit down, you idiot.' Swami thrilled at being called an idiot. 'If you get up again I will cane you,' said the teacher. Swami sat down, feeling happy at the promise. The teacher then asked, 'I am going to put a few questions on the Mughal period. Among the Mughal emperors, whom would you call the greatest, whom the strongest and whom the most religious emperor?'

Swami got up. As soon as he was seen, the teacher said emphatically, 'Sit down.'

'I want to answer, sir.'

'Sit down.'

'No, sir; I want to answer.'

'What did I say I'd do if you got up again?'

'You said you would cane me and peel the skin off my knuckles and make me press it on my forehead.'

'All right; come here.'

Swaminathan left his seat joyfully and hopped on the platform.

The teacher took out his cane from the drawer and shouted angrily, 'Open your hand, you little devil.' He whacked three wholesome cuts on each palm. Swami received them without blenching. After half a dozen the teacher asked, 'Will these do, or do you want some more?'

Swami merely held out his hand again, and received two more; and the bell rang. Swami jumped down from the platform with a light heart, though his hands were smarting. He picked up his books, took out the letter lying in his pocket and ran to the headmaster's room. He found the door locked.

He asked the peon*, 'Where is the headmaster?'

'Why do you want him?'

'My father has sent a letter for him.'

'He has taken the afternoon off and won't come back for a week. You can give the letter to the assistant headmaster. He will be here now.'

'Who is he?'

'Your teacher, Samuel. He will be here in a second.'

Swaminathan fled from the place. As soon as Swami went home with the letter, Father remarked, 'I knew you wouldn't deliver it, you coward.'

'I swear our headmaster is on leave,' Swaminathan began.

Father replied, 'Don't lie in addition to being a coward...'

Swami held up the envelope and said, 'I will give this to the headmaster as soon as he is back...' Father snatched it from his hand, tore it up and thrust it into the wastepaper basket under his table. He muttered, 'Don't come to me for help even if Samuel throttles you. You deserve your Samuel.'

---

*peon: headmaster's assistant

Kid in a Bin
Robert Carter

From opening till closing time, Anthony lives inside the wooden flip-top rubbish container which houses the plastic rubbish bags at McDonald's. His skin has become whiter and his brown hair is long and greasy; his eyes are cat-sharp. He is a bit over a metre tall which allows him to stand up straight inside the bin. In the mornings there is plenty of room for him to stretch, scratch, turn around or even curl up and doze. By mid-afternoon the empty foam cartons of Big Macs and cheeseburgers and McFeasts swell the plastic bag and choke out the light and space, forcing him either to stand thin against the back wall or to lean into the rubbish, until one of the counter crew changes the bag.

At different times, Anthony touches his finger against the inside of the used chicken containers which are made from cardboard and have a small piece of tissue paper where salt sticks to the splotches of grease. Old men use the most salt, followed by boys, girls, older women and younger men. The least users are younger women – about the age of Miss Tomagin, Anthony's third-class teacher, last year. By licking the salt stuck to his finger, Anthony guesses the age and sex of the chicken-eaters. When the cartons come through the flip-top bin, he touches, tastes and guesses the owners before they reach the exit door. Anthony likes to watch the customers. For a really good look he waits for the flip-top lid to be pushed inwards by a depositor, otherwise he has to be content with one horizontal slit and two perpendicular ones about a centimetre wide surrounding the lid. Anthony's world comes in slices.

At 11.30pm the night manager switches the air conditioning off, closes and locks the restaurant, and Anthony comes out to make his dinner and prepare lunch for the next day. There is a mouse who lives in an empty Quarter-Pounder box alongside Anthony. They go in and come out, mostly at the same times. Anthony calls the mouse Nigel.

It is Sunday, 11.40am. Outside the wind spits needles of rain. The customers are bursting through the doors, shaking like washed dogs, and laughing. Anthony is almost asleep in his bin – the air is humid and smells of sodden shoes and wet hair. Outside his bin is a boy exactly the same height as Anthony. The boy sees Anthony's eyes as he pushes his tray of rubbish through the swing-top. He pushes the flap again, and Anthony ducks down inside. He is too late, the boy sees his head disappearing behind the garbage. The boy pushes the flap once more and then reaches his arm in as far as he can in the direction of Anthony's disappearing head. His arm is too short to reach Anthony. The boy's mother sees what he is doing and shrieks at him to get his hand out of the filth. The boy goes to his mother.

'There's a kid in there.'

'Sit down, or I'll slap you.'

'There's a kid in the rubbish box, I saw his head.'

'Wait here, I'll get you another Coke.'

The boy waits for his mother to reach the counter and then goes back to the bin. 'Hey, you in there.' He tries to see inside by holding the flap open. 'What are you doing in there? You're not allowed in there.' A group of high school girls are giggling and nudging each other to have a look at the boy talking to the rubbish box. 'Why don't you come outside?' the boy says. The high school girls splutter into their thick shakes. The boy's mother returns with the drink, which she decides to give him in the car.

'It's probably a cardboard clown, or something,' she says.

'No it isn't, it's got real hair and real eyes, and it moves.' The boy's mother sees the high school girls looking at her and drags the boy out into the rain.

Inside the bin, Anthony eats one of the three Junior Burgers he prepared the night before. He watches the boy being dragged to the door, and the Coke being spilled as the boy looks and points back towards him. Anthony eats very slowly. Nigel is not in sight but Anthony pulls off a thumb-sized chunk of bun and places it in his box.

A newspaper comes through the flap and Anthony rescues it, saving it for later, when the shop is empty. Almost every day something to read comes into his bin. He has a small collection of torn-out newspaper items and one colour magazine article which has a picture of him, his mother and father and his sister. The newspaper ones have pictures of him alone. He carries them all in the pocket of his jeans, which are so tight that he has long since stopped doing up the top stud. The newspaper cuttings have begun to crack and split along the crease lines, from repeated opening and folding with greasy fingers. The magazine article is his favourite. Throughout stretching days in the dark bin, he feels the wad squeezed into his pocket, waiting for the eaters to go and the noise to stop. On wet nights the closing of the store takes longer. The floor is washed twice by the tired counter crew whose lips press together and whose name tags flop in time with the swing and pull of the mops.

Anthony listens for the sequence; air conditioner shut down, lights out, door lock click, and total quiet, except for the refrigerators humming downstairs. He waits several minutes in case the night manager has forgotten something and because he likes to anticipate the coming pleasure. He opens the hinged side panel of the bin from where the rubbish bags are removed and steps out into the customer area. The space rushes at him. Anthony closes his eyes for a few moments and then slowly opens them.

His legs and back are stiff and tight. He sits at a side booth made of blue plastic and watches Nigel run to the kitchen. It is still raining outside, he can see the drizzle sliding down the outer windows. With just the dull security lights on, he can see no further than the glass boundaries of the store. Once, earlier on, he attempted to look further by cupping his hands against the window and pressing his face against the pane, but all he could see was black, with some tiny lights too far off to matter, and some moths beating against the car-park lights.

He goes to the men's toilet, switches on the light and empties his bladder into the stainless steel urinal. He washes his face and moves it from side to side in front of the hot-air drier. Holding his hair back, he inspects his face reflected in the mirror. There is a tiny freckle-like spot on the bony bump of his nose, which he feels gently with his fingers, screwing up his eyes for a closer evaluation. The remaining skin is the white of his mother's scone mixture before it was cut into circles with a tumbler and shoved into the oven. Anthony leaves the toilet and goes into the kitchen. From under the refrigerator he takes two containers of orange juice. He switches on the hamburger griddle and the french fry vat and sits at the booth near the security light. From his pocket he pulls out the newspaper and magazine articles. He opens them carefully, bending the folds backwards and pressing them into flatness on the table top. With his fingernail he levers up the edge of the foil top sealing the orange juice and tears it away; some drops spill on the newspaper. He brushes them away with his sleeve and reads again under his photograph, with his finger sliding along beneath the words.

> *EIGHT-YEAR-OLD BOY STILL MISSING*
> The search continues for eight-year-old Anthony O'Neal who disappeared from his home on August 9th. A police task force has interviewed Anthony's school classmates, neighbours and relatives with no leads to the missing boy's whereabouts. Anthony's mother…

The griddle is hot and it is time to cook. Anthony stops reading and folds the articles back into his pocket. Outside he can hear the rain spatting at the glass, and the trucks changing gear in the distance. Nigel is running underneath the tables.

Anthony leans against the rubbish bag; he wants to go to the toilet and regrets drinking too much orange juice in the night. He concentrates on the customers through the slits. A tall lady with six children has come to have a birthday party. The children put on cardboard hats and make noises with balloons; one of them squeals every time the others take their attention from him – he is the birthday boy who shouts at his mother when he spills his thick shake across the table. His mother mops at it with table napkins and tells them he can have another one. He throws a piece of lettuce at the child opposite him who has turned his head away.

At the table alongside the birthday party sits a man and a girl. They are not talking, the girl has her back to Anthony and eats her chips one at a time and licks her fingers after each one. The man reads the *Saturday Morning Herald* and Anthony can see only the backs of his hands and the top of his head. As the man lowers his paper to talk to the girl, Anthony wets himself. It is his father, except that he looks older and his skin looks greyer. The girl is his sister, Meredith. Anthony feels for used paper napkins in the garbage. He finds some and attempts to blot up the urine before it leaks under the wooden bin and out into the customer area. Some of it escapes and sneaks across the floor and under the seat of the birthday boy.

Anthony presses his eye up against the horizontal slit. It is his father. Meredith appears to be bigger than he remembers. The floor crew supervisor discovers the leaking bin and dispatches a mopper to fix it. Anthony wriggles around to the other side of the bin to avoid detection when the side panel is opened. There is something he wishes to tell his father. A message he wants to pass to both of them. He takes an unused napkin from the bin and feels around until he locates a sundae container with some chocolate flavouring still in the bottom. He dips his forefinger into the container and prints his message in chocolate letters across the napkin delicately, careful not to smear the sauce all over the paper; he places it in an empty Big Mac box and watches through the crack. When everyone in the customer area is looking at something other than his bin, Anthony flicks the Big Mac box through the swinging flap and onto his father's table. Meredith jumps and showers chips over her father's paper.

'Someone threw a Big Mac at me,' she says.

'What?' Her father puts down his paper and collects the loose chips.

'Someone threw this at me,' she says again, picking up the box and looking towards the birthday party group. She opens the box and takes out the napkin, unfolding it carefully. She wrinkles her face at the chocolate sauce.

'Throw it in the bin, Meredith,' he says.

'It says words, Daddy.'

'What do you mean?'

'The chocolate says words.'

'Let me see.' He reaches for the napkin. 'It does too.'

'What does it say?'

'It says, 'STAY … OUT … OF … THE … something …STAY OUT OF THE … SUN.''

'What does that mean, Daddy?'

'I don't know.' The man's face looks puzzled. He stares at the birthday party group for a long time. There is no one else close enough to have thrown a box onto their table. He places the napkin and the box and the stray chips onto a tray and goes to Anthony's bin. He tilts the opening flap and tips the tray's contents in. Anthony has a close-up flash-view of his father's face. He sees the same ache as he sees in the men's toilet mirror. He watches his father and sister disappear through the exit door.

And the days and nights pass. Anthony's father and sister do not come into the restaurant again. Nigel becomes sick from eating rat poison and a lot of his hair falls out. Anthony drinks less orange juice and keeps checking his face in the toilet mirror. He cuts his hair with scissors from the manager's office. One night the manager comes back an hour after closing. Anthony is in the toilet. He switches the light off and hangs onto the clothes hook behind the door of the second toilet cubicle. The manager goes to his office. Anthony waits behind the door. There is a new message written on the back of the toilet door. He has not seen this one before; it says, 'Flush twice – the kitchen is a long way off.' Anthony does not understand the message. If the manager comes into the toilet, Anthony will lift his feet off the ground by holding onto the clothes hook. There is no sound coming from the manager's office. Anthony waits.

He thinks of being inside his bin curled up against the fat of the plastic garbage bag, with the murmur of customers and FM music filtering through – impregnable. The fear of being discovered outside his shell is worse than nakedness – worse than peeling the rind of his sanctuary.

Anthony feels something brush against his ankle. In the darkness, his eyes search for movement. It is a large tom cat. The manager has brought his cat to hunt for Nigel. Anthony thinks that Nigel will die quickly this way. He kicks the cat in the stomach, anyway. It hisses and runs out of the toilet.

Within an hour the manager is gone. The restaurant is safe again and Anthony prepares his next day's lunch. He sees Nigel run into the kitchen and he smiles about the big cat. Waiting for the oil to heat, he spreads his collected articles on a table top – he smoothes the magazine one, and looks at the picture of his family. He remembers when it was taken – on Meredith's fifth birthday, she got a bicycle with trainer wheels and it was in the background of the photograph. Anthony remembers giving her a large hazelnut chocolate which got left in the sun and which stuck to the foil and would only bend and stretch, rather than snap off in pieces.

Where the paper has been creased, some of the letters of the words have come away but this does not disturb Anthony; he has memorised most of them. He slides his finger under the words beneath the picture of his family. He reads aloud as he was taught in school, and sounds out the difficult words which, like many messages to Anthony, don't make much sense.

Missing schoolboy, Anthony O'Neal, pictured here with his parents and sister, Meredith, was last seen at his home on August 9th. Police believe his disappearance may be related to the death of his mother six weeks earlier. Mrs O'Neal died of metastatic melanoma, of which she was diagnosed six months previously. (Malignant melanoma is a virulent form of skin cancer caused in most cases by exposure of skin to the sun.) A large number of reported sightings of Anthony have been investigated by the police, with no success to date. Fears for the boy's safety have increased as no indication of …

The griddle is hot and it is time to cook.

Anthony peers out through the horizontal slit in the bin. It is cold outside and the faces of the seated customers go pink around the cheekbones from the warm McDonald's air. The rubbish comes in, tipped from its plastic trays. Anthony waits with Nigel for the store to close.

Death and the Boy
Retold by Anthony Horowitz

West Africa was gripped by the unrelenting hand of famine. Its arid breath whispered over the land, blighting the crops and blistering the livestock. Its shadow fell across the villages, stretching ever further in the remorseless sunlight. The water holes shrivelled and dried up. The mud hardened then cracked. Wherever the people went, black flies followed, sucking the last drops of moisture from the corners of their eyes and mouths. If famine was the king, the flies were its most loyal knights.

It was a cruel time. Every minute of every day became an exhausting struggle to find food, to break into the unyielding earth for water, to save the pathetically withered things that had been root vegetables or plants. The people struggled and prayed for rain. They knew they would survive. They had been through it all before.

But in one village there was a young boy who could work no longer. He had not eaten meat for so long (he thought) that he had forgotten what it tasted like. He was tired of the daily labouring, tired of seeing the blank determination that hung on the faces of his friends and relatives. And so one day he left the village, slipping away into the jungle to find his fortune – or at the very least, to renew his acquaintance with the flavour of meat.

For three days he walked without stumbling on so much as a parrot that he might pop into a pot. But on the third day, just as he was about to turn round and go home again, he came across something very peculiar. There were forty or fifty black ropes – at least, they looked like ropes – running along the jungle floor. The ropes ran in both directions for as far as he could see. Acting on impulse, puzzled as to what they might be, the boy decided to follow them and accordingly turned to the left.

He walked for more than a mile before the mystery was explained. The ropes weren't ropes at all. They were hair. And the boy had followed them to the scalp of their owner.

It was, of course, a giant. He was sitting outside a mud hut (from a distance, the boy had mistaken the hut for a small mountain) fast asleep. The giant was pitch black, the same colour as his remarkable hair, and this made the whiteness of his teeth seem all the more brilliant. These were the first things the boy noticed. The second was that despite the famine, the giant looked remarkably well fed.

The boy was just wondering whether he should stay where he was or head for home as fast as his feet would carry him when he became aware of a movement. The giant's eyes had opened, and he was regarding the boy with a sort of tired puzzlement.

'What are you?' he demanded, yawning.

'Please sir … I'm a boy,' the boy said. 'I didn't mean to wake you up. I was looking for meat.'

'How did you find me?'

'Well, sir … I followed your hair.'

'You mean, you've been haring through the jungle?'

The giant roared with laughter at his own joke, the sound making the ground vibrate. The boy laughed too, although he hadn't actually thought it was very funny. But then, when somebody one hundred times as big as you makes a joke, it's probably a good idea to laugh.

'If you want meat,' the giant said, when he had calmed down, 'I will give it to you. But you will have to earn it. You will have to stay here and work for me.'

And so the boy remained, sweeping and chopping

wood for the fire. And in return for these simple tasks, the giant was true to his word and fed him with as much steak as he could eat.

There came a time, however, when the boy became homesick. It had been months since he had seen his parents and his village and so he asked the giant for permission to take a short holiday.

'Of course,' the giant said. 'But you must send me someone to take your place while you're gone.'

'I'll do that,' the boy promised and, packing his bag full of meat for the journey, he set off through the jungle.

His family was delighted to see him when he got back and were astonished to find him looking so plump and healthy. His brother in particular pressed him to say what had happened.

'If you really want to know,' the boy told him, 'I can help you. How would you like a job where in return for the lightest of tasks you got more meat than you knew what to do with?'

'I'd love it!' the brother said.

Then the boy told him about the giant and the hut in the jungle. The brother naturally leapt at the opportunity to take his place and set off at once.

'By the way,' he asked, just before he left, 'what is this giant of yours called?'

'His name is Owuo,' the boy said.

Now Owuo is a West African word. And it means death.

Six weeks passed; more than enough time to cure the boy's homesickness. The trouble with home was that there still wasn't any meat and worse still, his parents expected him to join in the household chores, which meant far harder work than he had got used to with the Owuo. So one day he packed his bag again and followed the path of hair back to the giant's hut.

He had expected to see his brother there, but to his

surprise there was no sign of him. The giant, however, was unperturbed.

'He left a couple of days ago,' he explained. 'Like you, he got homesick. I'm surprised you didn't cross paths in the jungle.'

'I'd have thought he'd have waited for me,' the boy said.

'Forget him!' the giant cried. 'I've been waiting to tell you a new joke. Have you heard the one about the Krachian, the Salagan and the Zulu…?'

Time passed as pleasantly as it had before. The giant seemed perfectly content even though the boy did precious little work. And meanwhile the boy ate so much meat that he became quite fat. But once again, the only fly in the ointment was that he missed his brother and his parents. So, gathering his courage, he asked the giant if he could be allowed a second holiday.

'Very well!' the giant said. 'But this time I wonder if you could send me a young girl to take your place? In fact…' (and here he winked) '…I have it in mind to take her as my wife. If you could rustle up a pretty girl, I'd like to marinate her.'

'Did you say … marinate her, sir?' the boy asked.

'Did I?' The giant coughed and blushed. 'I meant *marry* her. I want to marry her!'

It was with a slight but indistinct feeling of uneasiness that the boy returned to his village. This time he was greeted with a little less pleasure. For his brother had disappeared. Despite what the giant had said, he had never returned home.

Nonetheless, the boy didn't mention the giant – for he was afraid that he would be forbidden to return to the hut if he did. It was only when he was talking to his sister one evening that he mentioned Owuo and in particular his desire for a wife.

'A wife?' the sister repeated. 'If I were the wife of this

Owuo, I would never have to work again. Like you, I could eat meat all day long.'

'Yes, but…' the boy began uncertainly.

'How do I find him?' the sister interrupted.

Although the boy still felt uneasy about it, his sister forced him to describe the path of hair, and the next morning she left, taking a servant with her.

This time the boy only waited a fortnight before he followed her back to the giant's hut. It was with a sinking feeling that he found Owuo sitting by himself, gnawing a bone.

'You're back early,' the giant said.

'Yes,' the boy replied. 'My sister…?'

'I haven't seen her or her servant for a week.' The giant tossed the bone over his shoulder. 'But I expect they'll turn up soon. Get yourself some supper, my boy. You must be hungry after your journey.'

The boy wasn't hungry, but nodding his thanks he went into the giant's hut where the meat usually hung, out of the sun. As always, the ground was littered with bones and it was as he stepped over these that he stopped, a wave of ice rippling through his body. His eyes bulged. His hair stood on end. The skin at the back of his neck tried to creep onto his shoulders.

There was a bracelet made of red beads around one of the bones. He would have recognised it anywhere, for he had made it himself. He had once given it to his sister as a birthday present.

That night, as soon as it was dark, the boy tiptoed away from the hut and then, his heart pounding, raced through the jungle, crashing blindly into the undergrowth, hardly caring where he went. He didn't stop until he had somehow reached his village and then he was so breathless that it was an hour before he could tell his parents what had happened.

The grief of the villagers at the loss of three lives was mingled with horror when they heard how Owuo had dealt with his victims. As one, they marched into the jungle, carrying with them flaming torches to light their way. The boy went with them for although nobody had said as much, he knew that he was to blame, and there was nothing he would not do to make amends.

It was by the light of the torches that they came upon the hair, more like snakes now than ropes as it twisted through the night. Then the boy had an idea.

'Owuo is too big for us to fight,' he cried. 'Let the fire do our work for us.'

And so saying, he seized a torch and thrust it into the hair.

Like a burning fuse, the hair hissed and crackled, carrying the fire on a winding path through the jungle. The villagers followed close behind. And so it was that they arrived at the hut just in time to see Owuo erupt in flames. One moment he was sleeping peacefully, the next he had disappeared in a crimson inferno. His screams were like the wind in a thunderstorm. But then it was all over and only a great heap of white powder showed where he had lain.

However, rummaging around in the ashes, the boy came upon a small bottle that Owuo had kept hidden in the very hair that had been his undoing. There were just four drops of a transparent liquid in the bottle and realising that whatever it was must be magic, he allowed three of them to fall on the bones in the giant's hut. In an instant, to the great rejoicing of the villagers, his brother, his sister and the servant-girl sprang to life, apparently none the worse for having been chewed up, swallowed and digested.

'Now – what shall I do with the last drop?' the boy asked.

'Wait…' his father said.

'No' his mother cried.

'You idiot!' the villagers yelled.

For the boy had upturned the bottle over the ashes of the giant.

A puddle formed in the middle of the ashes, bubbling and hissing. A wisp of smoke curled poisonously upwards, writhing in the moonlight. Slowly, hideously, an eye took shape. It opened, then gazed balefully at the boy who staggered back, terrified.

But that was all. Although the potion was powerful enough to restore a human life, it could manage no more than one eye of the giant.

In Togoland, where this myth originated, the people believe that the eye is still there, and that whenever it blinks, someone, somewhere in the world, dies. And because there is so much dust in the country, it blinks often. And one day, they say, the eye will blink for you…

The Old Woman Who Lived in a Cola Can
Bernard Ashley

Not all that long ago, and not so far away, there was an old woman who lived in a Cola can. 'All right,' you'd hear her say, 'the place *is* small, definitely chilly in December and scorching hot in July – but the floor never needs a coat of polish, and there's no dark corners where a spider can lurk.' The old woman reckoned it wasn't a bad place for a home, especially seeing there wasn't a penny to pay in rent.

One day, though, she went in for a telly, and she suddenly saw all sorts of things she'd never seen before. She saw all the adverts and loads of films – but instead of making her happy, all the new things only made her mad. She shouted and swore and shook her fist at the programmes.

'Rotten shame! Rotten shame! 'Tain't fair – it ain't fair!' she created. 'Why should I make do in this tinny little place when there's some lucky devils got nice flats in brand new tower blocks, with lifts to take them up and chutes to send the rubbish down? What's wrong with *me* I'd like to know? Why can't I have a chance to be choosy?'

She went on like that for ages, banging and clanging inside her can – till one day, by a stroke of luck just before her voice gave out, someone special heard her from the road: a flash young man who had won the pools and was looking for ways to get rid of his money.

He couldn't get across the grass to her quickly enough.

'Gordon Bennett, darlin', what a noise, what a *girls and boys*! But I heard what you was shoutin', and I've got to say I do feel sorry. I do. I feel choked, *prodded an' poked*. But say no more, girl, an' just keep your pecker up. Give us a couple o' days for some wheelin' an' dealin', watch out for the motor – an' we'll see what we're gonna see!'

So the old woman said no more. She switched off her telly, kept her eyes glued to the road, and before the milkman had been round three times, the flash young man was back, sitting in his motor and calling out across the grass.

'Come on, love, get out of the can! Jump in the car, the old *jam jar*, and come along o' me. I'll soon sort you out.'

She didn't need telling twice. She jumped in his car, just as she was, and before you could say knife, there she was in the town, in a nice little flat in a brand new block, with a lift to take her up and a chute to send the rubbish down.

And she was over the moon with delight. But she clean forgot to say thank you to the flash young man. And anyway, he had shot off to get on with his spending. He'd gone to the races, and smart sunny places, to Catterick, Corfu and Crete. But after a while, when his mouth ached with smiling, he thought he'd go back and see how the old woman was getting on.

And what did he hear when he got there? The tinkle of friendly teacups, a few contented sighs like the summer wind in net curtains?

Not a bit of it. Just the slamming of doors and shouts enough to wake the caretaker.

'Rotten shame! Rotten shame! 'Tain't fair – it ain't fair! I'm just about up to *here*, miles off the ground in this poky little flat – when there's some folks in the know got houses in streets, and their own front gates, with cars out the front and patios round the back. What's wrong with *me*, I'd like to know? Why don't I get the chance to be superior?'

The flash young man listened to every word she said. He kept dead quiet till he'd heard everything: then he put his eye to the spy-hole and he shouted through the door.

'Cheer up, doll,' he pleaded, 'no need for all that. Say no more, girl, and keep your pecker up. Give us a couple o' days for some wheelin' an' dealin', watch out for the motor – an' we'll see what we're gonna see!'

So the old woman said no more. She stopped banging doors, kept her eyes on the parking-bays, and before the kids had ruined the lifts three more times, the young man was back, leaning on his bonnet and calling up at her balcony.

'Come on, love, get down them stairs! Jump in the motor, the old *haddock an' bloater*, and come along o' me. I'll soon sort you out.'

She didn't need telling twice. She ran down the stairs, jumped in the back, and before she could say Jack Robinson, there she was in a neat town house in a proper little street, with car out front and a patio round the back.

She was over the moon with delight. But she clean forgot to say thank you to the flash young man. And, anyway, he'd shot off to get on with his spending. He'd gone to casinos, and sporting club beanos, to Monte, Majorca and Maine. But after a while, when his hand hurt with winning, he thought he'd go back to see how the old woman was getting on.

And what did he hear when he got there? The contented creak of an old cane chair, the sound of soft singing to Radio Two?

Not a bit of it. Just the slam of a swing-bin being attacked and shouts which ran to the end of the road.

'Rotten shame! Rotten shame! 'Tain't fair – it ain't fair! Here am I shunted off in this common little house – when there's some people live it up in tree-lined cul-de-sacs, with nicely spoken neighbours and a man to do the grass.

What's wrong with *me*, I'd like to know? When do I get a chance to be posh?'

The flash young man heard everything she said, then he rang upon her chimes. 'Heaven help us, love, what a state! What a terrible *two-an'-eight*! We can't have this. Give us a couple of days for some wheelin' an' dealin', watch out for the motor – an' we'll see what we're gonna see!'

So the old woman said no more. She stopped kicking-in the kitchen and packed her bags instead. And before she'd carried the dustbin through three times the flash young man was back, elbow on the dashboard and tooting at the door.

'Come on, girl, leg it over that gate! Jump in the Bentley, the old *gently-gently*, and come along o' me. I'll soon sort you out.'

She didn't need telling twice. She slammed herself into the car with her hat in her hand, and before she could say one o'clock, there she was in a double-fronted house in a cul-de-sac, with nicely spoken neighbours and a man to do her grass.

And she was over the moon with delight. But she clean forgot to say thank you to the flash young man. And, anyway, he'd shot off to get on with his spending. He bought up some pubs and three football clubs, United, Juventus and York. But after a while, when he got fed up with watching other people run around, he thought he'd go back and see how the old woman was getting on.

And what did he hear when he got there? The plop of fresh coffee being poured for the vicar, the rinsing of hands to get spoon polish off?

Not a bit of it. Just the rip of a radiator off of a wall and shouts loud enough to divert the traffic.

'Rotten shame! Rotten shame! 'Tain't fair – it ain't fair! Here am I overlooked in this middle-class place, when

Lords and Ladies have mansions in big country parks, and servants to send off to Harrods. What's wrong with *me*, I'd like to know? When do I get the chance to be Upper Crust?'

The flash young man caught every word she said, then made his way round the back.

'Hold your horses! Half-time!' he called through the tradesmen's entrance. 'You'll make yourself sick, *Uncle Dick*! Say no more, girl, and keep your pecker up. Give us a couple of days for some wheelin' an' dealin', watch out for the motor – an' we'll see what we're gonna see!'

So the old woman said no more. She put a few favourite bits into a suitcase – and by the time she'd turned three collecting-tins away from her door, the flash young man was back, purring into the driveway and breaking the beam on her burglar alarm.

'Come on, love, let's move it. Jump in the Jag, the old *boast an' brag*, and come along o' me. I'll soon sort you out.'

She didn't need telling twice. She shot in as fast as the speed of greased lightning, and before she could say hell for leather there she was in a mansion, a duchess no less, with servants to send off to Harrods and a tiara to put on her head.

And she was over the moon with delight. But she clean forgot to say thank you to the flash young man. And, anyway, he'd shot off to get on with his spending. He bought up an airway to make a cheap fare-way for tourists on trips to the States. But after a while, when he got fed up with being pointed at, he thought he'd go back and see how the old woman was getting on.

And what did he hear when he got there? The click of a croquet ball sent through a hoop, the flow of a pool being filled?

Not a bit of it. Just the sound of a summer-house being

destroyed, and shouts loud enough for three counties to hear.

'Rotten shame! Rotten shame! 'Tain't fair – it ain't fair! Here I am, just a two-bob old duchess down here, when there's SOMEONE WE KNOW with a crown on her head! What's wrong with *me*, I'd like to know? When do I get the chance to be Royal?'

The flash young man took note of what the old woman said, then he made an appointment to see her.

'Your Grace, what a row! What a *bull and a cow*! You are comin' on strong. But I know what you mean, so you don't need to say another word. Give us a couple of days for some wheelin' and dealin', watch out for the motor – and we'll see what we're gonna see!'

So the old woman said no more. She threw her tiara into the pool, kept her eyes peeled for the car with no number, and before she had time to sack three of her maids, the flash young man was back, gliding up towards her in his blue Rolls-Royce.

'Come on, ma'am,' he invited. 'Jump into the Roller, the *top hat an' bowler*, and come along o' me. I'll soon sort you out.'

She didn't need telling twice. She got into the back, cocked her head on one side, and started waving away out of this window and that. And before she could say, 'It gives me great pleasure,' she was there.

Back in her home in the Cola can: where, yell as she liked, she lived for the rest of her life.

But she never saved up for a telly again – and she wouldn't have said thank you if you'd given her one.

Sharlo's Strange Bargain
Ralph Prince

In Glentis Village, when people notice that you love your belly, they often say: 'You belly goin' bring you to de same en'* like Sharlo.' And then they will tell you the story of Sharlo and his strange bargain. It's an old, old story, and they say it's true. This is how it goes:

There once lived a man in Glentis Village named Sharlo. Some called him 'Long-belly Sharlo', because he loved food too much. Others called him 'Sharlo the Fifer', because he was the best fife player in the village. The fife was made from bamboo in Sharlo's own secret way, and it was the sweetest fife the villagers had ever heard. They believed that the music he played on it was the sweetest in all the world.

One afternoon Sharlo was returning home after working in his lands in the mountain. He was on the lower slopes, but still a long way from home, when a heavy shower of rain began to fall. He sheltered under a tree, but he got slightly wet all the time. The rain poured in torrents all afternoon and evening, enveloping the mountain in a thick, white sheet.

When darkness gathered, Sharlo felt cold and miserable. So he took out his fife and played it. He played all the old songs he could remember – songs of the old folk when they lived in the mountain, songs of the fishermen in Glentis Village, sad songs and merry songs. All these and more he played and played, sweeter than he had ever played before.

---

en: end, fate

Then suddenly he stopped playing. Right before him appeared a tall, red man. Sharlo was astonished, for he had not seen where the man had come from. 'Go ahead playing,' said the man. 'You played so sweet that I came up from down yonder to hear you.'

Sharlo asked him who he was, and the man said that everybody knew him. Sharlo then looked at him closely to see if he really knew him. The man seemed neither young nor old, but ageless. His skin was red and looked like the skin of a boiled lobster. His hair was white and flowing. His eyes were red, and they glowed as if fires burned within them. 'Never seen you before,' said Sharlo, after looking at him searchingly and long.

'You will soon remember who I am,' declared the man, 'and you will get to know me more, Sharlo.'

'How you know me name?' asked Sharlo, in surprise.

'Aha!' laughed the man. 'I know everybody, Sharlo – everybody in this world!'

Meanwhile Sharlo was still getting wet, so he edged up closer to the trunk of the tree. But the rain ran off the man's body like water sliding off a duck's back.

'Would you like to come down to my place for shelter?' asked the man.

Sharlo wondered where that place was. But he was wet, and above all, hungry, so he agreed to go, hoping to get some food there. The man led the way and Sharlo followed. As fast as the man walked, a hole opened in the mountain before him, going downwards all the time.

At last he stopped. Sharlo found himself in a large, oven-like room with fires burning along the walls. It was so hot that his clothes soon became dry and he had to take off his shirt; but the man was not even sweating.

He offered Sharlo a chair before a table, and then sat facing Sharlo. The man said nothing, but watched him intently. Sharlo yawned several times, expecting the man to offer him something to eat. But the man just watched him intently and said nothing. At last Sharlo could bear it no longer. 'You got any food?' he asked.

'Plenty,' the man replied. 'I was waiting for you to ask for some.' He then put a large, empty calabash* on the table before Sharlo.

'What would you like to eat?' asked the man, smiling.

'Anyt'ing,' answered Sharlo.

'Just say what you want,' the man explained, 'and this magic calabash will give it to you. But you must say it in rhyme, like this:

'Calabash, calabash, food time come;

Bring, bring pepperpot an' gee me some.'

And so Sharlo did as the man said, and repeated the rhyme:

'Calabash, calabash, food time come;

Bring, bring pepperpot an' gee me some.'

And then like magic, hot pepperpot instantly sprang up in the calabash, filling it to the brim. Sharlo was amazed. His eyes bulged. But already his mouth was watering.

'Have a bellyful,' said the man. 'Eat your pepperpot – it's yours, all yours.' So Sharlo ate and ate, until his stomach was full and the calabash was empty. Then he licked his fingers.

The man then asked Sharlo to play the fife for him. As his stomach was full, Sharlo played even sweeter than before.

'You play wonderfully,' said the man, smiling. 'I wish I could play as sweet as you.' And he borrowed the fife and played a tune. To Sharlo's surprise the man played beautifully, though not half as sweet as he.

'A wonderful fife you have here,' said the man, rubbing his hand over the keys. 'Mmmm hmmm. A wonderful fife.'

---

calabash: food container

But Sharlo was hardly listening. He was gazing at the calabash and imagining how wonderful it would be if he could have one like it, to give him all the food he wanted.

'You seem to like the calabash, Sharlo,' the man remarked.

Sharlo smiled.

'Would you like to have it?' asked the man.

Sharlo smiled again.

'Very well,' said the man, 'then we can make a bargain.'

'A bargain?' asked Sharlo, in surprise.

'Yes,' replied the man, rubbing his hand over the keys of the fife, 'a bargain that we must keep secret.'

'Wha' is de bargain?' asked Sharlo.

'You take my calabash,' the man explained, 'and I take your fife.'

Sharlo considered the matter for a while. He wanted the calabash, but he didn't want to part with his fife. He had had it since he was young. It was the best fife in the village. And playing it was his greatest joy – next to eating. He hesitated, unable to make up his mind.

'Come, Sharlo,' said the man, 'be sensible. You can always get another fife, but never another calabash like this again.'

'Even in hard times,' the man went on, 'this magic calabash will give you all the food you want. Think of the fungee and saltfish; the dumplings and pork; the rice and meat; the pepperpot; the souse; the ackee – all these and more are yours, all yours, just for the asking – and the eating.'

These were the very dishes Sharlo loved most. And with the calabash so near, the temptation was too great.

'All right,' he said at last, 'gimme de calabash an' tek de fife.' And so the man gave Sharlo the calabash and kept the fife.

He then led Sharlo back up the hole. The rain was over. 'Mind you, Sharlo!' said the man as they shook hands, 'keep our bargain a secret – otherwise it will be hell with me and you.' Sharlo promised to keep the bargain a secret, and they parted.

As he walked home Sharlo wondered who the strange man was. But he soon dropped the matter from his mind as he thought of the magic calabash he had got all for himself. And to test it again he said:

'Calabash, calabash, food time come;
Bring, bring ackee an' gee me some.'

And he ate the ackee all the way home.

From then onwards the calabash provided Sharlo with all the food he fancied. But from that same time he stopped cultivating his mountain lands or doing any other work. He did not get another fife, for he did not love music any more. All he now lived for was to eat.

So as the weeks passed he waxed fatter and fatter, and he became bigger than anyone else in Glentis Village. His face was round like the dumplings he ate every day, and it became so fat that he could barely open his eyes. His body took on a barrel-like bulge, and his belly sagged over his belt like that of a pig hanging down. Six months went by, and life for Sharlo went on like this – no work, no music, and food in abundance whenever he wanted.

Then hard times struck the island. There came a long drought and life became hard for the people of Glentis Village. Many of them starved, and sometimes their only food was sugar-cane. But Sharlo's magic calabash continued to give him all he wanted. He ate more than ever, sometimes feasting like a king.

Then suddenly his dream of endless feasting ended. It happened this way. The drought had been on for three months and the villagers began to wonder where Sharlo was getting food from. For he did not go to the shops to buy anything. And his neighbours did not see him cook anything. So when he walked down the road people sometimes asked: 'But Sharlo, how you doin' so well an' we ketchin so much hell?'

This always made him laugh. And as he laughed his eyes would close, and his many chins would tremble and his belly would shake like that of a pig when it runs. But all he would say was: 'Shut-mout' no ketch fly.'*

So the source of his food supply remained a mystery, even to his best friends. An old friend of his called Zakky was constantly trying to find out, but Sharlo would not tell. All he would say was: 'Shut-mout' no ketch fly.'

But as the drought wore on, Zakky became desperate, for he had a wife and ten children to feed. One evening he went to see Sharlo. Sharlo was finishing a calabash of calaloo. He swallowed the last mouthful, rumbled a belch, licked his fingers, stretched his legs across the floor, and peered out of his fat, fleshy eyes at Zakky.

'Ay Sharlo,' Zakky called out, 'wha' do?'

'Ah bwoy,' Sharlo replied, 'me dey – jus' a-mek out.'*

'Man you nah mekkin out,' Zakky declared, 'you fat like mud.'

Sharlo rumbled another belch and laughed as he clasped his fat hands across his barrel of a stomach. Zakky gazed hard at the calabash for a while and then said: 'But Sharlo, man you wort'less.'

'Wha' me do?' asked Sharlo.

'Man, you wort'less,' Zakky repeated. 'You know me an' me wife an' ten pickny* an' dem a-dead fo' hungry, an'

Shut-mout' no ketch fly: a closed mouth will not reveal any secrets
me dey – jus' a-mek out: I am just surviving
pickny: children

you never one time say, "Here Zakky, tek dis food fo' all-you nyam*!" '

'Me food too poor fo' you,' said Sharlo.

'Too poor!' cried Zakky, 'an de calaloo you jus' done nyam smell so nice? Man, me could nyam de calabash full o' calaloo clean right now!'

Sharlo gazed at Zakky's thin body and bony face and hollow eyes, and felt sorry for him. 'All right, Zakky,' he said, 'ah givin' you some food, but you mustn' tell anybody 'bout it.' He then recited the magic rhyme:

'Calabash, calabash, food time come;

Bring, bring calaloo an' gee me some.'

Immediately the calabash was filled to the brim with hot calaloo. Zakky was amazed. He stared at the calabash with bulging eyes. At last he said, 'Well, well, well! So dis is how you getting' food – by obeah!'*

'Is not obeah,' Sharlo replied.

'Is by obeah!' Zakky repeated. 'So you become a big obeah man, eh Sharlo?'

'Is not obeah,' Sharlo repeated in defence. 'Zakky, ah tell you is not obeah.' Sharlo was afraid that Zakky would spread the word around, because it was an awful thing in Glentis Village to be called an obeah man.

'Well, if is not obeah,' said Zakky, 'wha' it is eh? Tell me, Sharlo, how else you get dis calabash full o' calaloo but by obeah?'

'All right, Zakky,' replied Sharlo, 'ah will tell you, but you mus' keep it a secret. Go ahead eat de calaloo, is good food; ah goin' tell you de story.'

Zakky began to eat the calaloo, and as he ate, Sharlo told him the whole story. When he mentioned the tall, red man, Zakky laughed. After a while he laughed so

---

nyam: to eat
obeah: sorcery

much that he had to stop eating. By the time Sharlo had finished his story, Zakky was rocking with uncontrollable laughter, holding his sides as if they were bursting.

'Wha' mek you laugh so?' asked Sharlo.

'Is de bargain you mek wid de devil,' Zakky replied.

'De devil!' cried Sharlo, in surprise.

Zakky then explained that the tall, red man who appeared suddenly as from nowhere, and who lived in that hot place down below, and who had provided such a magic calabash, could have been no one else but the devil. It was only then that it slowly dawned on Sharlo that the man he had made the bargain with was indeed the devil.

Sharlo had always heard that it was not wise to deal with the devil, and he began to imagine what the devil had meant when he said it would be hell if the bargain was not kept a secret. He became fearful, and shuddered. He begged Zakky again and again not to tell anyone about the bargain.

Zakky promised to keep the secret. And to encourage him, Sharlo repeated the magic rhyme several times and filled a bucket of food for him to take home, and told him to return anytime for more.

The next morning Zakky and his wife and their ten children went to Sharlo's home with the empty bucket for more food. They met the house open, with the front door broken off.

'Sharlo!' Zakky called.

No answer came.

Zakky and his wife and their ten children went inside.

'Sharlo!' Zakky called again, 'a whey you? A whey de calabash?

No answer came.

They searched all over the house, and outside in the

yard, and everywhere in Glentis Village, but neither Sharlo nor the calabash was anywhere to be seen.

The villagers searched for him for a long time, even in his mountain lands. But Sharlo was never seen again.

The Ghost Train
Sydney J. Bounds

Billy Trent ran down the lane towards the common, sandy hair poking like straws from under his cap, eyes gleaming with excitement. The common blazed with coloured lights, post-box red and dandelion yellow and neon blue. The evening air throbbed with the sound of fairground music and his pulse beat in rhythm.

He reached the entrance and passed beneath a banner that read:

BIGGEST TRAVELLING FAIR IN BRITAIN!

A jolly, red-faced man dressed as a clown called to him. 'On your own, son? Enjoy all the fun of the fair!'

Billy nodded eagerly, too excited to speak, for the fair came only once a year and he'd saved hard for the occasion. Almost a pound's worth of change clutched tight in his pocket, he darted between the coconut shy and a hamburger stand, chair-o-planes and swing boats. He paused, fascinated, in front of the carousel with its pairs of magnificent horses going round and round and up and down. He stared up in awe at the big Ferris Wheel revolving in the sky, trying to make up his mind which to try first.

There were dodgem cars, and a snaky switchback ride. Music played, fireworks exploded in cascading showers of light. The smell of cotton candy tempted him. For Billy it was the best night of the year, until…

In a shadowy empty space behind the fortune teller's tent, he found himself between two youths dressed in jeans and leather jackets studded with stars.

The big one with the scarred face gripped Billy's arm. 'Hi kid, we'll give you a break – you can pal up with us tonight. It's more fun sharing things. I'm Ed, and my mate here answers to Higgy.'

Higgy, fat and pimply, sniggered in a way that gave Billy gooseflesh. 'Hi, pal, glad to meet yuh. Ed and me's broke, and that ain't much fun, so I hope you've got plenty of cash. We're all pals together, see?'

Billy shook his head, mute. He had a sinking feeling in his stomach and his hand tightened around the coins in his pocket as he stared up at the two older boys. He decided he didn't like either of them.

Ed's big hand tightened on his arm till it throbbed with pain. 'Now come on, share the loot – reckon we'll all go on the dodgems first, okay?'

Billy gasped desperately. 'You're hurting me. All right, I'll pay for you to have one ride, if you promise to leave me alone after that.'

Big Ed laughed meanly. 'That's no way for a pal to talk. Share everything, that's our motto, ain't it, Higgy?'

'You bet. Now then, kid, hand it over.'

As Billy slowly brought his hand from his pocket, Ed relaxed a fraction, grinning at Higgy. Instantly Billy twisted like an eel, slipped from Ed's grasp and ran off as hard as he could go.

'Little perisher,' Ed shouted angrily. 'Just wait till I get my hands on 'im – I'll break 'is flaming neck!' With Higgy at his heels, he gave chase.

Billy pushed his way into the fairground crowd, panting, looking for someone – anyone – he knew. But there were all strangers, intent on enjoying themselves and oblivious to his trouble. The music blared loudly and bright coloured lights flashed.

Billy glanced back; the two youths were still after him, and Ed's scarred face looked savage. He ran behind a wooden hoarding and found himself trapped between the Wall of Death and the switchback ride. It was dark and he could see no way out. The roar of motor-cycle engines was deafening; even if he shouted, no one would hear. He hunted for somewhere to hide as Ed and Higgy turned the corner and spotted him.

Dim blue lights spelled out:

GHOST TRAIN

Billy could just make out the shape of a miniature steam engine with six open cars in the gloom. The cars were empty. There seemed to be no one about, not even at the pay desk.

As the train began to move towards the dark mouth of the entrance tunnel, Billy ran forward and sprang into the car nearest the engine. He crouched low, but …

'There he is!' Ed shouted, pointing. Higgy right behind him, he put on a spurt and they reached the train in time to scramble aboard the last car.

The Ghost Train gathered speed as it rumbled into the tunnel. In the darkness, Billy gulped as he looked up to see the luminous skeleton-figure of the engine driver grinning back at him. But he was too scared of his pursuers to be really frightened.

Then Ed and Higgy started to climb over the empty cars towards him.

The track wound and the cars swayed and rattled. Cobwebs brushed Billy's face. An eerie green glow illuminated the tunnel and a tombstone beside the track; the stone lifted and a cowled figure rose with a dreadful wail.

It was night-black again and a woman's scream echoed. In a phosphorescent glow, a headless phantom stalked towards the engine, vanished. Chains clanked and something evil-smelling dripped from the roof. A bat-thing swooped, hissing.

The dark came again. Then a lightning flash revealed a fanged monster.

The train rattled on through the blackness. A red glow from a fire showed three witches stooped over a cauldron; as the train passed, the nearest lifted her death's head and cackled with laughter.

Suddenly Billy was aware that the two bullies were no longer interested in him. The skeleton-driver of the Ghost Train had left his engine and was moving steadily back along the cars toward them. Ed's face had lost its savage look. Higgy's eyes no longer gleamed with malice.

As a bony arm extended, skeletal finger pointing, they backed away. Empty eye-sockets stared sightlessly at them, jaws gaped in a toothless snarl. A hollow voice intoned: 'Beware!' And, scared stiff, Ed and Higgy scrambled back to the last carriage.

The ride ended and Billy got away smartly. As he mingled with the crowd, he saw Ed and Higgy – their faces white as chalk – hurrying towards the exit. They'd had enough.

Billy looked for the Ghost Train, but he could not find it now.

Left alone, he enjoyed all the fun of the fair. He went on one ride after another until he'd spent his money. He was very happy as he turned to go home.

On his way out, the clown called to him again. 'What did you like best, son?'

Billy Trent paused and thought. 'The Ghost Train,' he said.

The clown's jolly red face paled. 'But there's no Ghost Train now! Used to be one, with Old Tom driving, dressed all in black with a skeleton painted on. Then one day a youngster fell off the train and Tom dived after him. Killed he was, saving the lad. After the accident, the boss scrapped it – so you must have dreamed that.'

But Billy was quite sure he hadn't.

Polyphemus the Cyclops
Retold by Barbara Leonie Picard

After their ten-year-long war with the men of Troy was ended and the Trojan city had fallen in flames and smoke, the victorious Greeks gathered together their booty and their prisoners; and when the great King Agamemnon, who was in charge of all the Grecian host, had given the word, one by one all those leaders of the Greeks who had survived the fighting boarded their ships and set sail for home.

Among them was Odysseus, king of the little island of Ithaca, lying off the mainland of Greece. He and his men put out to sea in twelve ships of fifty oars, their white sails unfurled and their blue-painted prows thrusting through the waves as the wind filled the sails: nigh on sixty men on board each ship. And the heart of every man was happy as he thought how at last, after ten weary years of battle, he would once again see Ithaca, which was his home.

The next land that they reached was the country of the Cyclopes, a simple, savage folk, of more than human size, who never tilled their land, or built ships or houses, or traded with other nations. Instead they lived in caves in the rocks and spent their time pasturing their flocks on their rich green fields.

Just off the mainland lay a wooded island, the home of many wild goats, and to this island the twelve ships came on a misty night. The men disembarked and slept; and in the morning, when the mist had cleared, they saw opposite them the land of the Cyclopes, and were surprised, for in the fog they had not imagined the mainland to be so close.

All that day they rested from their labours on the sea
and feasted on the flesh of the island goats. Keeping a
careful watch upon the land, Odysseus was just able to
make out the huge flocks of sheep and the cattle of the
Cyclopes, browsing in the fields, and the smoke from the
fires of the herdsmen. 'Tomorrow', he said, 'I shall go
with one ship to the mainland and see who lives in that
rich country. It may well be a friendly folk who will give us
welcome hospitality after our days at sea.'

Accordingly, in the morning Odysseus sailed to the
mainland and beached his ship on the shore below a
rocky cliff which towered above their heads, with shrubs
growing among the rocks and little yellow wallflowers
springing from every cleft.

Close by, half-way up the cliff and approached by a
zigzag pathway, was the opening of a wide cave, half-
hidden by laurel bushes and surrounded by a wall of huge
stones. It was plain to see that the cave was someone's
home, and picking out twelve of his best men, Odysseus
set off up the cliff carrying a skin of the finest wine he had
on board, as a gift for whoever might live there.

Beyond the wall they found a courtyard with pens for
sheep and goats; though the pens were empty when they
saw them, for the flocks were out at pasture with their
owner.

'There is no one here,' said Odysseus. 'Let us wait in
the cave for the shepherd to return.' And they passed
beneath the glossy foliage of the overhanging laurels and
went inside.

Within, the light was dim, but when their eyes grew
used to it, they saw that the huge cave held many pens of
lambs and kids, all separated according to their ages.
There were, too, great pails of milk, and cheeses stacked
in baskets hanging from the roof. But for all this
abundance of good food the cave did not seem a friendly

place, and Odysseus' men urged him to let them take as many cheeses and lambs as they could carry and return at once to the ship. But he would not hear of this. 'We could not rob a stranger in his absence,' he said. 'Besides, when he returns it may please him to give us far more gifts than thirteen men can carry off, and it would be folly to miss the chance of filling our ship with savoury cheeses and tender kids which we might share with our comrades waiting on the island.'

So they remained in the cave. And towards evening the herdsman returned with his flocks. He was as tall as three men and broad, with but one eye in the middle of his forehead; and as soon as Odysseus and his men caught sight of him they knew that they had been unwise to wait.

He came to the entrance of the cave and flung inside a huge bundle of logs, large branches lopped from tall pines and oaks, as faggots for his fire; and in terror the Greeks fled to the darkest corner of the cave and hid themselves.

The monster penned his rams and goats in the courtyard, and drove the ewes and she-goats into the cave for milking, blocking the entrance with a great stone. And even his sheep and goats were larger than any Odysseus had ever seen before.

When the milking was over, the monster penned the ewes with their lambs and the goats with their kids, and set himself to make a fire from the wood he had brought home. As soon as he had a blaze, he was able to see, by the light of the leaping flames, Odysseus and his men, crouching in the very farthest corner. 'Who are you, strangers?' he asked in a voice like thunder.

For all his terror Odysseus stepped forward and answered boldly enough. 'We are Greeks, sailing home to Ithaca from the war with Troy. The winds have carried us somewhat from our course, and we have come to you in the hope that you may be our host until we can set sail once more.'

The giant roared, 'I am Polyphemus the Cyclops, and I entertain no guests unless it pleases me. But tell me this, where have you beached your ship? Is she close by?'

Odysseus suspected the question and guessed the Cyclops meant harm to his ship and the men guarding her, and he answered cunningly, 'Our ship was wrecked upon your shore, and only I and these twelve men escaped alive from the sea.'

But Polyphemus gave no word of sympathy in reply. Instead, he seized a man in each hand, and dashing out their brains against the rocky floor, he tore them in pieces and ate them for his supper before the eyes of their horrified comrades. Then after drinking several large pailfuls of milk, he lay down by the fire to sleep.

Odysseus would have drawn his sword and crept upon him while he slept and killed him, but that he knew it would be impossible for him and his men to move away by themselves the great stone that blocked the opening of the cave. So, terrified, they waited all night, whispering together and trying to devise some means of outwitting the cruel monster.

At dawn Polyphemus rekindled the fire and milked his ewes and goats again. That done, he snatched up two more of Odysseus' men and ate them as a wild beast might have done. Then he rolled aside the great stone from the mouth of the cave and drove out his flocks; and replacing the stone once more, he went towards the mountain pastures, whistling cheerfully at the thought of the good supper which awaited his return.

Odysseus and the eight men left to him sat down beside the fire to think how they might escape the fate which would surely be theirs unless they could find a way to leave the cave; and at last a plan came to Odysseus. In the cave there lay a long pole of green olive-wood, drying so that it might serve the Cyclops for a staff. From this pole Odysseus hacked off with his sword a piece the length of a tall man, and set his companions to sharpen one end into a point and harden it in the fire.

'Tonight,' he said, 'when the monster sleeps, we will heat the wood red-hot and with it put out his single eye.'

When the point of the stake was hard and sharp, they hid it, and then chose by lot the four men who should help Odysseus use it in the night.

When evening came the Cyclops returned with his flocks, and this time he drove all the sheep into the cave, rams and ewes alike, and penned them safely. When he had milked the ewes and goats he thought of his own supper, and seized two more men. While he sat by the fire eating them, Odysseus poured out a huge bowlful of the wine he had brought with him, and coming forward, offered it to Polyphemus. 'Such wine as this our ship held before it was wrecked upon your shores,' he said. 'Come, taste of it and tell me if you think it is not good.'

The Cyclops took the wooden bowl and drained it at one draught. He held it out to Odysseus. 'Give me more,' he said.

Odysseus filled it a second time, and again the monster drank. 'Give me yet more of your wine, stranger,' he demanded, 'and tell me your name, that I may give you a gift in return.'

A third time Odysseus filled the bowl and the Cyclops drank. 'My name is No-one,' said Odysseus. 'Tell me now what gift you will give to No-one in exchange for his good wine.'

'I will eat you last of all your comrades. A few more hours of life, that shall be my gift to you.' And with a mighty laugh that echoed through the cave Polyphemus lay down beside the fire; and made drowsy by the wine, he fell deeply asleep at once.

Odysseus thrust the stake into the embers and held it there until it was red-hot, then taking it, he and the four men on whom the lot had fallen drove it deep into the Cyclops' eye.

With screams and with shouts of rage Polyphemus awoke and pulled the stake from the socket of his eye, and wildly flinging his arms about and stumbling around the cave, he tried to catch Odysseus and his friends, who crouched trembling against the wall.

The neighbouring Cylcopes who dwelt in caverns nearby heard his cries, and coming to his cave, stood outside the great stone and called to him. 'What ails you, Polyphemus? Why do you wake us with your cries? Does someone steal your sheep or kill you?'

'Good neighbours,' said Polyphemus, 'it is the cunning wiles of No-one that are killing me.'

'If no one is killing you,' answered the neighbours, 'you must be sick, and illness comes from the gods, and we can be of no help to you. You have woken us in vain. May your sickness have left you by the morning.' And they returned to their own homes.

But the Cyclops groped his way to the entrance of the cave and pushed away the great stone, and sitting down in the doorway, waited to catch any of the men who might try to pass him; so that they saw that there was no escape for them that way.

At the far end of the cave Odysseus and his companions made whispered plans; and taking reeds from Polyphemus' bed, Odysseus bound together eighteen of the finest rams in threes, with one of his six men tied beneath each middle ram. Then he himself laid hold of the largest ram of all, a great creature with a splendid fleece, and lay underneath it, clinging on and hidden by the shaggy wool that hung down from its broad sides.

By that time it was dawn, and the rams were eager to be grazing in the rich pastures. Bleating, they moved together to the entrance of the cave, where Polyphemus felt across the back of each one as it came to him, before passing it through into the courtyard. But he never thought to feel beneath the animals, so the six men went safely out. Last of all to come was the leader of the flock, walking slowly under the weight of Odysseus, clinging to its fleece.

As Polyphemus felt its back he spoke to it. 'My good ram, you are ever the foremost of the flock, leading the others to their grazing ground. Why are you last today? Are you grieved for your master, blinded by wicked No-one, and would stay to comfort him? I would that you could speak and tell me where he hides, that wretch who took away my sight. But go, dear ram, join your companions in the fields.' And Polyphemus moved his hand aside and the ram stepped through the opening into the sunlight, bearing Odysseus.

Once outside the courtyard, Odysseus freed himself from his hiding-place and went to release his companions. Then hastily they drove the sheep down to the ship and their comrades waiting on the shore. With no delay they stowed the flock on board and set out to row back to the island where the fleet was moored.

A little way from the shore Odysseus stood up in the ship and shouted with all his might, 'Now indeed, wicked Cyclops, do you know what ills your cruelty to helpless strangers has brought to you.'

Polyphemus heard him and came out from his cave in fury, and breaking off a huge piece of rock he flung it into the sea in the direction of Odysseus' voice. It fell in the water by the bows and the great waves made by its fall washed the ship back towards the shore; but Odysseus seized a long pole and pushed off again, and his men fell to rowing hard once more.

Again Odysseus stood up to shout his taunts to the Cyclops, and though his men tried to restrain him, for they feared another rock might be cast at them, he called out, 'Polyphemus, if anyone should ever ask you how you lost your sight, you may tell him that Odysseus, king of Ithaca, put out your eye.'

And again Polyphemus tore off and hurled into the sea a rock. But this time it fell to the stern of the ship, and sent her rushing forward to the island.

Once safely with the men from his other ships, Odysseus divided the sheep among them, a fair share to each. But his companions allotted him the fine ram by the help of which he had escaped, as an extra gift, because he was their leader, and because he had saved six of his men from the Cyclops.

Chicken
Mary Hoffman

It was hard to say when the group became a gang. Perhaps it was when Mark Mason tried to hang around with us and we froze him out. Or perhaps when we started calling ourselves The Inliners. Definitely we were a gang by the time of the leadership struggle or there wouldn't have been a struggle to start with. And we'd never have been so stupid as to do the dares.

We had all known each other since Nursery. Alfie and I had hung out together since before we were born actually, because our mums were best friends and they'd gone into the hospital to have us on the same day.

Dylan, Jamal and Leon all live within a couple of streets of Alfie and me. (I'm Rick, by the way.) We all learnt to swim together in the local kiddie pool, all went to birthday parties at each other's houses dressed as Power Rangers or Ninja turtles, all went up to the Juniors at the same time, all played football on the common, all went to Woodcraft and went camping together, all got our first inline skates the same Christmas.

So had a lot of other kids, of course, but our group had been special from the beginning, enjoying in-jokes and making up a sort of private language that kept our other friends at a slight distance. We were all among the oldest and biggest in our year, because we all had birthdays close to one another in September. Maybe that made us look more like a gang, like hard men. But there was nothing about us to worry our parents or our teachers – until we got into Year 6.

For the first time in our lives we were facing being split up. Alfie's parents were thinking of moving and Dylan's were putting him in for the Grammar school. Only me, Jamal and Leon were sure of being in the same secondary school and it made the whole group edgy. Maybe that's when we became a gang.

It was late October when the dares started. I suppose it was my fault really. We were just mucking about when I dared Alfie to steal some fireworks from Patel's. That's when Alfie should have said no and the whole thing would have stopped before it started. Then maybe *it* would never have happened. But he didn't.

It was pathetically easy. Mr Patel is a nice trusting man whose daughter Sushila is in our class. Alfie managed to smuggle two Skyburst rockets out under his blazer while the rest of us chatted to Mr Patel about the local football team.

Later, when we set the rockets off on the common, everyone was a bit hyper. Maybe that's when the rivalry between Alfie and Dylan started. Alfie was capering round like a mad thing, the bright explosion of coloured light from the rocket dyeing his face green and purple.

'One Alfie Spencer, there's only one Alfie Spencer,' he was chanting.

'Knock it off!' grunted Dylan. 'It was only a bit of shoplifting.'

'Yeah, well,' said Alfie. 'But look who didn't do it.'

'No one asked me to,' said Dylan indignantly. 'I would've done it if it was my dare.'

'Yeah,' said Alfie.

'Go on then,' said Dylan. 'Dare me and I'll show you.'

'Yeah, dare him, Alf,' said Jamal.

Alfie thought for a minute. Not shoplifting again; that was too easy.

'Okay, Dyl,' he said slowly. 'I dare you to get Old Knickers trick or treating.'

'Old Knickers' was Mrs Nixon, our headteacher. By

common consent, her house was always avoided by trick or treat gangs at Hallowe'en. Mrs Nixon had strong views on what she called 'hooliganism'. And she made them very clear in assembly on November 1st.

'Much as I dislike that American import of tolerated blackmail called Trick or Treating,' she told the whole school assembly, 'I thought there were at least some rules to it. I thought children were supposed to ask which you'd prefer. Indeed I even had a bowl of fun-size chocolate bars ready by the door…'

Jamal and Leon turned to look at me. We had missed a trick there. Or rather a treat.

'But no one rang the bell,' continued Mrs Nixon, 'and this morning I discovered my car had been decorated with pink silly string and my garden hedge was festooned with loo paper.' She glared at us and Dylan stared straight ahead.

'Lame,' whispered Alfie out of the corner of his mouth.

And so it continued all term. There was the guy of Old Knickers that was burnt at the bonfire party. That was Jamal's dare. The kidnap of Cooper, who was the ginger cat belonging to our form teacher, Miss Jellicoe. That was Leon's, only he got caught, because he was covered in scratches. He wouldn't have hurt Cooper; Leon was soppy about all animals. He was supposed to have sent a ransom note for £20, but Cooper escaped and ran home.

Then there was the fire in a wastepaper basket, which set off the smoke alarms and called out the fire brigade. That was mine, I'm now ashamed to say, and it earned me a lot of admiration in the gang.

But the main rivalry was still between Alfie and Dylan. It got worse by the end of term, when Dylan sat the exam for the Grammar School. It seemed as if Alfie was determined to take him down a peg or two.

The Inliners were beginning to spilt into two. I could

feel it happening and I didn't like it. I always backed Alfie, of course, and Jamal tended to support Dylan. Leon was the most easy-going of all of us, and refused to take sides.

And now our parents were getting really concerned. Leon's had been horrified about the cat incident but he had managed to persuade them that it was just a practical joke gone wrong. The school had begun to suspect us because all the incidents were connected with our form and, being big and bad-looking, as I say, the suspicion naturally fell on us, even though we'd never done anything like this before.

Then Alfie twisted his ankle quite badly trying to abseil down the school wall. I have to admit that I was helping him, but I wasn't the one who had dared him to do it. All the dares now seemed to be between him and Dylan and they were getting worse. Alfie's parents asked a lot of awkward questions about what we'd been up to after dark that made him hurt his ankle, but at least no one saw us.

Then Dylan got horribly drunk doing the dare about having one glass of everything in his parents' drinks cabinet. His sick note said he had a tummy upset, but that was putting it mildly. I overheard my mum telling Alfie's it was alcohol poisoning and Dylan had had to go to hospital.

I tried to get Alfie to stop then, because it was clearly becoming dangerous, but he said it was Dylan's turn to dare him to do something next and he couldn't stop it because Dylan would call him chicken. Dylan came back to school looking very white and shaky and I saw him give Alfie an evil look at break-time. It was hard to believe that they had ever been friends.

And yet we were still all in the gang. Inliners for ever! We were all skating along the High Street together when Dylan said to Alfie, 'I dare you to take on the Terminator.'

If we hadn't been going downhill, I would have stopped. The Terminator was a boy at the comprehensive, about fourteen years old and already built like Arnie. He was Mark Mason's older brother, Tony, but everyone called him the Terminator and he liked it. Actually I don't know that he ever did anyone any damage, but he was well over six feet tall and made of solid muscle. No one had ever tried to bully Mark, let's put it that way. Alfie wouldn't stand a chance against him and Dylan knew it.

I sped up and came level with Alfie. He was looking almost as green as he had that night by the light of the stolen rockets.

'Are you mad?' I hissed. 'You're not really going to do it? You'll end up as dogmeat. I might as well call the ambulance now.'

'What's the matter, Alf?' taunted Dylan, whizzing past. 'Are you chicken?'

Alfie straightened his back and concentrated on weaving in and out of the shoppers. I could see he was going to do it.

He didn't let me in on the plan this time, so I couldn't even be around to help him when the massacre took place. I never knew what exactly happened, but a couple of days later there was a ring at my doorbell, and Alfie fell on the doormat. He looked terrible. He had a black eye, which was closing up fast, and a thick lip and blood all down his cheek.

'I did it, Rick,' he gasped, rolling over and clutching his stomach.

'I'll ring the hospital,' I said.

'No, don't,' whispered Alfie. 'Let me stay here. My parents'll kill me if they find out. Specially so soon after the ankle thing.'

'How do you think they're not going to find out, with you looking like that?' I demanded.

Fortunately the matter was taken out of our hands, because my mum came out and saw him. And that was that. She rang Alfie's mum and then drove him straight to Casualty. I was allowed to come too and Alfie's mum met us there. The grown-ups were white-faced and quiet in that way that's so much more scary than shouting.

Alfie refused to say who had done it. He had no broken bones, thank goodness, only bruising. But all hell was let loose just the same. Old Knickers had a field day in assembly, going on about bullying, and the whole gang was put on report – which was very unfair, seeing as we hadn't done anything to Alfie. Except for Dylan of course.

I honestly thought it would end there, as soon as Dylan saw Alfie's face. He looked a bit peculiar, as if he might throw up. And if Alfie had been prepared to give it up, it might have all stopped before the worst happened. But Alfie had just been given the pounding of his life, and he wasn't about to let Dylan off the hook.

Nothing happened for a week and it was nearly the end of term. I was beginning to breathe more easily. Alfie was a bit more quiet than usual but that was understandable. Then one day at break he took me to one side and said, 'Saturday afternoon. Silbury cuttings.'

My blood ran cold. I've often seen that written down, but that's actually what it feels like. As if icy water is being pumped through your veins. Silbury cuttings used to be notorious in our neighbourhood. A few years ago, a kid was killed on the railway line at Silbury cuttings. It was a result of a game of 'chicken' with the trains. Ever since then, it has been the biggest no-go area around. The number of lectures we've had in assembly about it, with the police as well, and the number of times our parents have spoken to us about it in their most serious voices – well, I just can't tell you how it made me feel to hear Alfie even mention it.

'You're kidding, right?' I said, knowing he wasn't.

'Never more serious,' said Alfie. 'Are you in, or not?'

I didn't know what to say. My mind was racing. My only hope was that the security was now much tighter round Silbury cuttings than it had been when the kid got killed. I swear Alfie could read my mind, because he reached into his bag and took out a pair of wire-cutters he'd pinched from his dad's toolbox.

I decided to play along with Alfie, till I could work out what to do. I told him I was in, then as soon as I could, I got Jamal and Leon on their own.

'Silbury cuttings!' said Jamal. 'No way! That's going too far.'

Leon agreed and I was hugely relieved. Surely if all three of us said no, we could stop it? I mean, we didn't have votes or anything, but it was three against two, always assuming Dylan would even accept the dare. We should have known better.

We caught up with Alfie and Dylan before school on Friday. They were standing near the gate, deep in conversation. I felt a pang; it was like the good old days when we were all just best mates. Until we got close to them and we could see the look in their eyes.

They just refused to listen. Dylan said Alfie had set us all up to put him off, because then he could call him chicken. He was particularly disgusted with Jamal. So I did the unforgivable: I told them I'd tell their parents.

Alfie and Dylan rounded on me with identical looks of fury.

'If you do,' hissed Alfie, 'it'll be the end of you and me.'

I thought about being friends since before we were born.

'And.' He added, 'it won't even stop us. We'll just do it another time, when they've forgotten about it. They can't watch us for ever.'

I felt absolutely paralysed. The best we could do was to say that we wouldn't be there and that we thought they were both mad. We walked away into the school building and that was the moment I knew the Inliners had ended for ever.

But, of course, I did go to Silbury cuttings on Saturday afternoon and so did the others. I think we couldn't bear not to know what was going on. We squeezed through the gap in the wire fencing that Alfie had made with his father's cutters. Then we slid down the embankment and hid behind some bushes. We could see them, Dylan and Alfie, standing by the railway line like a couple of trainspotters. My mouth was dry: I could hear a train coming.

It streamed past and I had no idea what had happened. It was all noise and speed and confusion. I realised my eyes were shut. When I opened them, I could have cried with relief. Alfie and Dylan were both still standing there. But they seemed to be arguing. I caught the words 'not ready' before the wind whipped them away and I realised it wasn't all over. Dylan was still going to do it. I saw him step onto the line.

I think I must have gone a little mad then. I went charging down the embankment yelling. I don't even know what I was saying or what I intended to do. Wrestle them both to the ground and sit on them till they came to their senses? I was no Terminator.

There was another train coming. I grabbed Alfie, gibbering and crying like an idiot. The train was getting nearer. Dylan just stood there, white and frozen. He wasn't going to make it.

'Dylan!' I screamed, but he didn't seem to hear me. I didn't dare grab him. I still feel bad about that. I still have nightmares about it. Dylan standing on the line like a statue, me rooted to the spot, unable to move as the train got closer.

It was Alfie who moved. I felt him wrench himself away from my grasp and hurl himself towards Dylan. And then the train rushed by. I couldn't see them, couldn't hear anything but the screaming of wheels on rails. The slipstream from the speeding train knocked me over and I was out of it.

I came round hearing the others crashing down the embankment. Jamal and Leon helped me up and we saw the other two across the other side of the line. They were lying on the ground with their arms wrapped round one another, and there was a lot of blood.

Suddenly, there were shouts behind me. Policemen came down the embankment, talking urgently into their radios. They must have called the ambulance because that came flashing and nee-nawing along soon afterwards. It turned out someone had seen the hole in the chainlink fence and dialled 999. The police must have called the station too, because no more trains came by while the paramedics carried Dylan and Alfie away on stretchers.

The local papers tried to turn Alfie into a hero. He told me that was the worst part, having everyone praise him for saving Dylan's life, when his life wouldn't have been in any danger in the first place if it hadn't been for Alfie. He feels nothing but guilt about what happened. After all, he was okay, physically, just very shocked and bruised. But Dylan, well, his foot was so badly hurt, they had to amputate it.

He can't skate so well with his artificial one, but he still does it. We all still see each other. Alfie's parents didn't move away after all, and Dylan didn't pass his Grammar School exam, so we all ended up at the comprehensive. The funny thing is, although we're all still friendly, it's Alfie and Dylan who are best friends now.

Me and Alfie aren't as close as we used to be. I thought at first it was because he felt he owed Dylan one, but once he told me that it was more as if they had gone through a bad illness together and survived. 'It was a kind of madness,' he said.

We are definitely not a gang any more. Just a group of friends, who've known each other since Nursery. We wouldn't dare be anything else.

Poinsettias
Beverley Naidoo

Marika thrust the glass jar up to Veronica's face.

'See this one Nicky!' she declared. 'Caught it last week!' Veronica stared at the coiled brown shape slithering inside the greenish liquid. She felt sick.

'You should have seen how blinking quick I was man! This sort are poisonous!'

Marika's eyes pinned her down, watching for a reaction. She didn't know which were worse, Marika's or those of the dead creature in the jar.

'Where did you find it?'

Her voice did not betray her and Marika began her dramatic tale about tracking the snake in the bougainvillaea next to the hen-run.

It was a valuable addition to her collection. Rows of bottles, all with the same green liquid, lined the shelf above her bed. Spiders and insects of various shapes and sizes floated safely, serenely, inside. Marika carefully replaced the snake next to another prize item – a one-legged chameleon, its colours dulled and fixed. Veronica remembered it alive. It had been the farm children's pet briefly until they had tired of capturing flies for it. She had even helped one whole Saturday, prowling around the cow-shed, sneaking up and snapping the over-fed blue-buzzers in cigarette tins. The next morning Marika and her brothers had decided to let the creature go free and get its own dinner. But when they had come to release the catch of the splintering old wood-and-wire hutch, the chameleon lay stiff and still. The three boys had wanted to make a special grave down in the donga* – but in the end Marika had persuaded them to let her preserve it.

The farm, a small-holding owned by Marika's parents, lay against a mountain in the middle of the Magaliesberg. As well as growing fruit and vegetables and keeping a few animals, the van Reenens let out a small cottage on the farm, mostly to city visitors. It was near enough to Johannesburg for Mr and Mrs Martin with their only child Veronica to get away from the ever-increasing hustle for short breaks. They were regulars, coming two or three times a year. In fact Mr Martin had been visiting since he was a child, when Marika's mother herself had been a small girl on the same farm. Veronica's own memories of the place stretched back for as long as she could remember. For years she and Marika had played 'house' in the donga behind the farmhouse. They had used larger stones for the walls, shifting around smaller stones as the furniture. In the past Veronica used to bring all her dolls, despite her mother's protests. Sensing Marika's envy, she had enjoyed saying which dolls could be played with. But since Marika's tenth birthday things were different.

Veronica had been taken by surprise. She had been sitting with the farm children on the wall of the stoep*, dangling her legs and kicking the brickwork with her heels like the others. Marika had been telling her about the disco which had been her birthday treat when Veronica had suggested that they go to the donga.

'Hey the girls are going to play dollies!' Marika's twin brother Piet had sneered. Slipping off the wall, six-year-old Dirk had rolled on the ground, kicking his legs in the air and cooing.

---

donga: deep ditch
stoep: veranda

'Gaga gaga! Mommy! Mommy! Change my nappy!'

Veronica had glared at him and he had pulled a face at her. She had fought to hold back her tears. Only Anton, the oldest, had not joined in, but called the others to leave the girls alone to their sissy games. Marika had reacted furiously.

'I'm not a sissy!' she had screamed after them. Leaving Veronica alone on the stoep, she had gone inside the house, slamming the door behind her.

When Veronica returned to the farm a few months later, Marika had begun her bottle collection. Veronica had also left her dolls at home, except for the eyelid-clicking, brown-eyed Margaret. But this time the porcelain head with brown painted curls remained tucked under the bedclothes and was spoken to only at night. She became Veronica's personal counsellor on the farm – a pale replica of Veronica's personal counsellor in town.

Back home in Johannesburg it was Rebecca, their maid, to whom Veronica confided. She was a far better listener than Margaret because she made sympathetic noises. With Veronica's mother often helping out at her father's office, or busy with Mothers' Union meetings, they spent a lot of time together. Whether she was cooking, washing, ironing or dusting, Rebecca was always prepared to chat. But she never came to the farm with them. Instead she went to visit her own children, living with their grandmother, a five-hour bus ride away.

Sharing secrets with Rebecca was fun, especially when Rebecca had let her visit her dim, tiny room in the servants' quarters at the top of their block of flats. It had started with her desperate desire to see the bedspread which Rebecca had been patiently embroidering for months on 'babysitting' nights when Veronica's parents went out. Although Veronica didn't think she needed to be 'babysat', she liked Rebecca's company. Together they would sit and talk at the table in the Martins' kitchen until it was her bed-time. She had watched the bedspread growing and, when it was finally completed, had begged and nagged to see how it looked on the bed. But before she could be taken, Rebecca had made her promise, 'Remember, you are not to tell your ma or pa!'

Because it had been a secret, everything had stayed fixed in her mind like a picture. The splendid bedcover draped over an old iron bed raised up high on bricks. A curtain across one corner of the room. Rebecca's cupboard. An orange crate table next to the bed, on which stood a photo of Rebecca's four children. Veronica had studied their smiling black faces to see if they looked like their mother, trying to match the faces to the names she asked Rebecca to repeat. The only one whose name she always remembered was Selo, the oldest, because he was exactly her age and his name was shorter than the others.

'Is this Selo?' she had asked, picking out the tallest of the children, who had a cheerful, cheeky grin.

'Oh yes, that's Selo! Always getting into trouble!' Rebecca had laughed, adding, 'But he's a good boy.'

Yet here on the farm there was no Rebecca. So it was to Margaret that Veronica confided about the snake's awful eyes. Of course if it was Rebecca, she would make some sounds to show how disgusted she was. Then they would laugh together at how stupid it was to keep all those dead creatures in jars.

But there was something even more important she needed to talk to Rebecca about. It was something Marika had said after she had put the snake back on the shelf. She had hinted strongly that her brothers had made up a test which Veronica would have to pass before she could go on playing with them. Marika herself had carried out a dare set by the boys. She would not say what it had been, it was so terrible. She was equally mysterious about Veronica's dare.

'I'm not allowed to tell … but you know our neighbour Jan Venter…?'

Marika had stopped and ominously refused to say anything more.

Big and burly – known for his flaming red beard, moustache and temper – children, and even adults, usually kept clear of Meneer Venter when possible. Veronica had seen him only once, when he had called to see Mr van Reenen to insist Marika's father mend the fence between them. He ran one of the biggest orange estates in the area and everyone knew that he threatened to shoot any trespasser on his land like he shot baboons. That was not to be taken lightly. Jan Venter was known to be 'fond of the bottle' and there had been talk about the disappearance of Mrs Venter a few years ago. Some people said she had just had enough of his temper and gone back to her own people in another part of the country. The rumour amongst the local children was that he had murdered his wife and buried her in front of his house – under a poinsettia bush which now had brighter than usual red flowers.

The next morning, instead of darting off early to look for Marika, Veronica hung back and waited for her parents before going to the farmhouse for breakfast. Marika and her family ate in the kitchen but the Martins were served their meals in the dining-room, beneath a pair of massive kudu horns and heavily framed photographs of Marika's grandparents. Mrs van Reenen followed behind the servant who carried the plates of steaming porridge.

'Still no sign of rain, but it'll be a nice day again for you all!'

She smiled and stopped to pass on some of the local

news, including talk of a leopard seen again on the mountain behind the farm.

Today Veronica took her time. When she came to her last piece of toast, she chewed it slowly. She was trying to think of a good reason to stay with her parents who were pouring second cups of coffee, when her mother said, 'You can be excused, Veronica dear. You can go off and play. You won't go near the mountain, will you?'

She nodded, pursing her lips together and got up. Her father ruffled her hair as she passed.

'Have a good day, Ronnie!'

He only called her that when he was relaxed. She just hoped Marika's brothers didn't ever hear it. Their jokes about 'Nicky' were bad enough.

Hoping the van Reenen children might still be at breakfast in the kitchen, Veronica headed for the opposite door, to the stoep. But they were already there on the wall, legs swinging, waiting. Anton, the oldest, was direct.

'We've made a new rule. Girls have to do a dare before they join our gang.'

Veronica stood rooted to the concrete floor. All the children except Anton were grinning. Dead-pan, he went on to explain that she had to climb through the barbed-wire fence into the neighbouring Venter estate and make her way across to the front of Jan Venter's farmhouse.

'You've got to get one of his poinsettia flowers. We don't have any this side, so you can't cheat!'

They would accompany her as far as the fence and wait for her to return.

There was no way out. If she wasn't part of the gang, there would be no one to play with. As they marched across the donga Veronica glanced at the spot where they used to play 'house' in the shade of the thorn trees. The stones were still there. It was like another world. Inside she felt cold and shivery even though her feet and arms were moving swiftly in step with the others and the sun's heat was already enveloping them. As they trudged in silence along the edge of the mealie field, nearing the wire fence, Dirk suddenly broke out into a jingle.

'Nicky, Nicky, looks so sicky!'

He was told sharply to shut up by the others.

'A dare is not a game! It's a serious thing you idiot,' Marika snapped.

At the fence Anton and Piet parted the barbed wire for Veronica to slip through. Anton pointed.

'The farmhouse is that way. At the end of the orange trees follow the road.'

Veronica cast a quick glimpse back at the group. They all had solemn faces except for Dirk who couldn't hide his little grin. She was already far down the line of orange trees when she heard Marika's voice ringing faintly behind her.

'Good luck, hey Nicky!'

Sounds of laughter seemed to follow.

For as far as she could see ahead there were only straight rows of trees, the deep green leaves and bright orange fruit silently glinting in the sunlight. They were not good cover. With her shadow darting from one tree's patch of shade to the next, her mind began searching wildly for what to say if she was caught. Could she pretend she was lost … or that she had a dog which had got lost? Or that she had come to warn Meneer Venter about the leopard on the mountain? Veronica could not imagine the big burly man with the flaming beard believing any of her stories. She almost wished the dare had been for her to go up the mountain instead.

Her mouth was dry, her body wet and sticky, her legs sprinting heavily. Sucking in small quick breaths, she jerked to a halt. The moments of rest brought a terrible panic. What on earth was she doing here, alone in the middle of Jan Venter's oranges? This dare was too dangerous. She should run back and tell the others it was unfair. She bet they wouldn't do it! Then she remembered Marika saying her own dare was too terrible to talk about. Perhaps she had just said that to frighten her ... But if she went back now, that would be the end of their friendship. Whatever could she do by herself on the farm? It wasn't worth thinking about. Lips pressed together, her eyes intently scoured the bushes ahead.

At last she could see she was coming to a dirt road. Peering from behind a tree, she studied how to make her way up it. On either side was a line of tall grey bluegums leading to a cluster of white-washed buildings. The furthest one seemed to be the main house. There was no poinsettia in sight, so the front had to be around one of the other sides. Behind the bluegums on the far side of the road, set a little back, were some huts – servants' quarters. Usually she hardly took any notice of these kind of buildings. They were just there, part of what you found on a farm. But now she was forced to scan the area around the huts very closely. Although there were some open doorways, they were too dark to see inside. No one seemed to be around, either on the road or in the workers' compound, but it would be safer to stay on the side where she was for as long as possible. A few large avocado trees would provide thick cover for a short stretch – and then she would have to trust to the bluegums and to fortune.

At last, in line with the main house, she crossed the road. Her shoes smacking against the sand pounded as loudly as her heart. Facing her was a door, leading to a backyard. She ducked down to creep past a window. A few paces more and she had reached the side of the raised stoep. On tip-toe she stretched to look. Still no one! Through the wooden railings she glimpsed a spray of pointed red flowers. The poinsettia was just around the corner! Making a final dash to the bush, she ripped off a flower at the stem. Milky white stuff spurted out on to her fingers. Not bothering to wipe off the stickiness, she turned to run. But a door banging, and fearsome shouting forced her to cower back next to the poinsettia bush and freeze.

'Jou bliksem! Ek sal jou moer!'*

It could only be Jan Venter. Veronica's Afrikaans was not very good despite the lessons at school. But she knew Meneer Venter was swearing and that 'moer' was 'murder'. Who was he going to murder now? Was she not perhaps already standing on his wife?

The commotion got worse. She could hear sounds of running and other people coming outside. An elderly woman in housemaid's uniform hurried down steps from the stoep close by to Veronica, without noticing her huddled against the wall. She was moaning softly to herself. Meneer Venter was shouting about people who stole from him. Everyone would see now what he did to thieves.

Veronica was trembling but she had to find out what was happening. She stretched forward to see around the corner. A small number of servants stood at a short distance from the massive figure – his face just a shade lighter than his blazing beard and hair. In front of him stood a black child with thin spindly legs, wearing a pair of torn khaki shorts, his eyes fixed on the ground. The man grabbed the boy's ear and jerked his head upwards, with his other hand forcing an orange into the boy's face.

'Kyk hierso!* Look at this! I'll teach you a lesson you'll never forget!'

Jou bliksem! Ek sal jou moer!: You scum! I'll kill you!
Kyk hierso!: Look here!

'Please Baas*, this boy has learnt his lesson. He won't do it again Baas. I will speak to him Baas!'

It was the old housemaid, her hands together as if in a prayer, pleading, moving nearer to Meneer Venter. His arm swept out, dismissing her.

'He must learn a proper lesson. Talking is not good enough!'

The old woman was insistent. 'He's only a child my Baas. Once the Baas was also a child!'

Meneer Venter turned on her now. 'You go too far now Lettie. Watch out or I'll give you a lesson too!'

The old woman covered her face with her hands shaking her head.

Meneer Venter shouted instructions to a couple of servants who disappeared through the side door. One came back with a wooden chair and the other with a cane. For a moment after his ear had been released, the boy looked around wildly. In the second that Veronica glimpsed his eyes, she almost called out. He looked like Selo, Rebecca's son, in the photograph! It couldn't be him, could it? Rebecca's family lived far away. But Rebecca had said Selo was always getting into trouble.

The boy was ordered to lean over the chair. One of the male workers was ordered to stand in front and hold him down. Meneer Venter took the cane. Veronica did not look after the first two strikes. The boy's cries pierced her ears. She was shivering all over. Her stomach heaved.

When the cries reduced to a soft whimpering, Veronica looked up. To her horror Meneer Venter was walking in her direction in a slow swagger. There was no time and no where to run. Standing transfixed, she dropped the flower in her hand. His eyes were odd, glazed, as if not seeing anything. Then, as he drew close, they flickered.

Baas: Master

'Jy is 'n van Reenen, ne?* Tell your father I'm satisfied with the fence.'

Before Veronica could even think what to say, he patted her hair lightly and walked on, up the steps and into the house. He had thought she was Marika.

Guiltily, Veronica looked down at the fallen poinsettia. She was aware of the old woman gently holding the boy, making soothing noises. The small assembly of servants were talking quietly amongst themselves. Hastily she picked up the blood-red flower. The milky oozing had stopped and sealed up the stem. Grabbing a branch above her, she snapped off four more stems, careless of the sticky sap. A flower each. Sprinting down the road, she passed the old woman and the boy who had begun making their way painfully towards the huts behind the bluegums. No sounds followed as she entered the orange trees. She stopped running. She could walk the rest of the way now and give herself time to regain her breath. Then she could present each flower quite calmly. She might even take the gang some oranges.

---

*Jy is 'n van Reenen, ne?: You're a van Reenen, aren't you?

The New Boy
Geddes Thomson

Tam was in a good mood that morning. His mum had had a big win at the bingo the night before. She had brought home some special fish suppers, two bottles of Irn Bru and a big red box of chocolates. A nice surprise on a Tuesday night, with the rain running down the windows, no money for the gas fire and the telly rotten as usual.

She had given Tam five one pound notes which now nestled in his jerkin pocket. It was a great feeling, pound notes in your pocket. He would pass the day thinking about what he would do with all that money. Better than listening to moany old teachers.

He was explaining all this to his mate, Alec, as they dragged their feet through the school gate, when he first saw the new boy.

Tam nudged Alec. 'Whose zat?'

'Doan know. Never seen im before.'

The new boy was surrounded by a crowd of first years. He was a big broad-shouldered lad with a sun-tanned face and dark curly hair. He was dressed in a fancy pullover and brown corduroys and he was wearing a tie. The first years seemed to be enjoying his company, because they were laughing and skipping about him like a pack of playful dogs.

Tam stopped and stared at the newcomer in *his* playground. He didn't like the way the first years were listening to the new boy's every word. Tam was used to younger boys looking up to *him* as a kind of leader.

'Hullo,' shouted the new boy.

'Talking tae me, son, or chewin a brick?' Tam shouted back.

The first years stopped their capering and edged away like cowboys in a western when the goodie and the baddie meet up in the saloon. The new boy was suddenly alone which didn't seem to bother him one little bit.

'Braw morning,' he said.

'*Braw Morning!*' Tam imitated. 'Who the hell ur you? Oor Wullie or somethin? Listen. We rule here, pal. Don't forget it. OK?'

Just then the bell went. The playground began to empty. Tam turned away and swaggered towards the technical block. He felt the crinkly pound notes in his pocket.

Tam didn't see the new boy again till the second last period of the morning – English. It was one of his better subjects. Mr Campbell wasn't as moany as the other teachers and there wasn't anything special to learn in English.

'Seasy,' he told Alec. 'Ah kin speak it, can't ah? No like that bloody French. Ivrybody should talk English. Wan languidge fur ivrybody.'

Alec decided there must be something wrong with that argument. 'Yiv goat tae huv different languidges. It's their culture n'at. How are aw the foreigners gonny learn English?'

Tam didn't answer because a snobby girl prefect with gold braid on her blazer had just brought in the new boy.

'See whit the cat's dragged in,' he whispered to Alec. 'Big heid the breid.'

The new boy was nearly as tall as Mr Campbell. He looked perfectly relaxed and smiled broadly, not the slight shy smile of an ordinary new pupil. Mr Campbell directed him to a seat at the back of the room beside Kathy Milligan.

They were doing a project about advertising. It was called 'The Hidden Persuaders'. Mr Campbell always had fancy titles like that for his English projects. But Tam quite liked him and usually he weighed in with a few answers just to keep him happy.

Today Mr Campbell was on about TV adverts, asking the class for their favourites. Tam, aware on the new boy somewhere behind him, put up his hand.

'Ah like the one about biscuits, Sir.'

Mr Campbell smiled encouragingly.

'Tell us about it, Tam.'

'Well it's these Mexican bandits an they rob a bank an the federales come an it's fur this biscuit.'

'I know the one you mean. Why do you like it?'

Tam decided to show off, show the new boy how gallus he was.

'Well, ah like the burds, Sir. Lovely burds in that ad.'

Alec spluttered with laughter, but Mr Campbell was not so easily put off. '*Why* do they have – young ladies – in the advert?'

There was a pause. 'Yes, Colin?'

Tam heard the voice of the new boy behind him. 'It's tae mak ye think the product is … glamorous. Tae … tae connect it wae nice ideas so that ye'll gae oot and buy it.'

Everybody turned round to look. They realised that he had put into words what had been vaguely going through their own minds.

Mr Campbell was delighted. 'That's a very good answer, Colin. A *very* good answer.'

But Colin wasn't finished yet. 'Tak this lassie aside me, Sir. Now if she was tae recommend biscuits oan the TV, I wid definitely buy them because she looks sae nice.'

Tam narrowed his eyes and glared. Kathy Milligan's dark head was lowered, but he could see her blush and smile. He had quite fancied Kathy Milligan for a long time and here was this character giving her the patter already.

Tam was never sure how to deal with girls. Once, in the

corridor, he had smiled at Kathy Milligan and punched her on the arm.

'Why did you do that?' Alec had asked.

'Ah – like er.'

'You *like* er!' Alec had laughed. 'Ye've goat a funny way a showin it. What would ye do if ye *didny* like er? Break er arm?'

Alec was nudging him. 'This guy's quite a character, Tam!'

Tam stared at Alec and chose his words carefully. 'This guy,' he said, 'is a *snob* and a *swot* and ah'm gonny sort him out.'

'He's big.'

'Aye, a big drip. Wears a tie, talks funny, gies good answers. He's a big,' Tam stopped, searching for the word that would sum up what he felt about the new boy. 'He's a big tube.'

'Kathy Milligan likes im.'

Tam suddenly realised that his so-called pal, Alec, was deliberately annoying him and didn't answer.

For the rest of the period he day-dreamed about how he would sort out the new boy.

The last period of the morning was PE. Once again the new boy was in his class. Tam watched him closely in the dressing-room and nudged Alec when the new boy took a pair of shining white shorts out of his duffle bag.

'Look whit snobby's goat.'

Tam wore his own black shorts under his jeans. He never carried anything to school, even a pencil. If you tried to carry things around they just got lost. And then there was trouble.

'Ah still think e's big.' It was Alec again. Sometimes Tam wondered why he bothered with Alec, because Alec wasn't normal. He supported Partick Thistle for a start. Partick Thistle!

Tam decided to needle his friend. 'See me an him. It'll be like Rangers and Partick Thistle. Nae contest. The bigger they are, the harder they faw.'

The PE teacher, Mr Simpson, appeared, bouncing a football on the stone floor. Big Sim he was called and he was hard as nails. That was why Tam never forgot his shorts.

'OK,' Big Sim said. 'Pay attention, lads. Football in the top playground and nothing above head height because of the windows. Got that?'

Big Sim's cold blue eyes flicked over them, one by one, looking for any boy without his full kit, but even wee Sammy, who didn't know the day of the week, had brought his gear.

Out in the playground they were divided into teams. Tam was pleased to see that he was in the opposite team from the new boy. Now he would show him who was the boss.

The game started. The orange football began to skid around the playground chased by players.

After a few minutes the new boy, who turned out to be a good player, dribbled towards Tam. As he went past Tam tripped him, making it look like an accidental late tackle. The new boy fell his full length on the concrete playground. His nose was in a puddle and his knee was bleeding. The white shorts were spattered with mud.

Big Sim came pounding up, blowing his whistle and waving his arms like a big-time referee as the boys crowded round the figure on the ground.

'Get back, you lot. Are you OK lad? Any damage?'

The new boy smiled. 'Ah'm fine, Sir. Ah've just skint ma knee. That's aw. Accidents happen, ye ken.'

But Tam sensed that the rest of them didn't think it was an accident. He heard Alec's whisper over his left shoulder: 'See you. You're mental!'

For the rest of the game he hardly got a kick at the ball, but the new boy's name began to ring out over the playground.

'Well done, Colin.'

'Nice pass, Colin.'

'Great goal, Colin.'

Afterwards, in the dressing-room, Tam pulled on his clothes without a word to anybody. He felt that somehow he had suffered a great defeat and he wasn't quite sure how it had happened. OK, he had tripped the guy. So what? That was nothing.

Five minutes later Tam sat in the shelter and watched the entrance of the PE building. He felt a tension that tightened his throat and neck so that he could hardly breathe.

At last he saw the new boy come out the glass doors and look around as if searching for something. Or someone.

Tam rose to his feet in the dark shelter. Slowly he walked out into the sunlight. The new boy saw him. He was waving something in his hand.

'Can ah see ye a meenit?' he shouted in that funny accent which grated on Tam's nerves.

'Ah suppose you can,' Tam shouted back, 'unless you're blind.'

The new boy was now standing in front of him. Alec was right. He was big. Tam had to look up into the broad brown face.

'The bigger they are the harder they faw.' That was what he had told Alec. It had been a favourite saying of his father's. 'The bigger they are the harder they faw.'

Tam clenched his fists inside his jerkin pockets.

'Something wrang?' the new boy asked.

'Aye,' Tam said. '*You*'re wrang. You've been wrang since the minute ah saw ye. Who are you? Where do you come frae?'

The new boy opened his mouth to answer and, at that moment, Tam jumped him in a flurry of swirling arms and thudding fists. He heard the new boy gasp in pain, but he also felt knuckles crash into his own face. Desperately, he grabbed his enemy round the waist and the two of them swayed and tottered round the playground like two drunk men until they crashed to the ground.

Tam had him locked around the waist in a vice-like grip, but the new boy had an equally strong hold on Tam's neck.

After a minute like this he heard Colin MacDonald say, 'You let me go and ah'll let *you* go.'

Tam strengthened his grip while he thought about this. It might be a trick. On the other hand, Tam could feel his strength slowly draining away. He decided he had better take the offer while there was still time.

'One – two – three!' And Tam let go and at the same moment felt the arms drop away from his own neck.

They lay side by side on the hard playground. Exhausted.

'Yer a bonny fighter,' he heard the new boy say.

'Yer no sae bad, yersel,' Tam had to admit.

'Oh an ah've goat something fur ye,' Colin MacDonald sat up and opened his big brown fist to reveal a heap of green paper. 'Ah fund them in the dressing-room. They're yours, aren't they? Ah wis comin tae gie them tae yi.'

The pound notes. No longer new and crinkly, but crushed and dirty.

They grinned at each other.

The Fight
Ruskin Bond

Anil had been less than a month in the town when he discovered the pool in the forest. It was the height of summer, and the school he was to join had not yet opened. Having as yet made no friends in the small town in the foothills, he wandered about a good deal by himself, into the hills and forests that stretched away on all sides of the town.

It was hot, very hot, at that time of the year, and Anil, aged thirteen, walked about in his vest and shorts, his brown feet white with the chalky dust that flew up from the ground. The earth was parched, the grass brown, the trees listless, hardly stirring, waiting for a cool wind or a refreshing shower of rain. It was on one of these tiresome days that Anil found the pool in the forest. The water had a gentle green translucency, and he could see the smooth round pebbles at the bottom of the pool. It was fed by a small stream that emerged from a cluster of rocks.

During the monsoon this stream would be a rushing torrent, cascading down from the hills; but during the summer it was barely a trickle. The rocks, however, held the water in the pool, and it didn't dry up like the pools in the plains.

When Anil saw the pool, he didn't hesitate to get into it. He had often been swimming, alone or with friends, when he had lived with his parents in a thirsty town in the middle of the Rajasthan desert. There, he had known only sticky, muddy pools, where buffaloes wallowed in the slush. He had never seen a pool like this – so clean and cool and inviting. He threw off all his clothes, as he had always done when swimming in the plains, and leapt into the water. His limbs were supple, and his dark body glistened in patches of sunlit water.

The next day he came again to quench his body in the cool waters of the forest pool. He was there for almost an hour, sliding in and out of the limpid green water, or lying stretched out on the smooth yellow rocks in the shade of the broad-leaved sal trees.

It was while he lay naked on a rock that he noticed another boy standing a little distance away, staring at him in a rather hostile manner. The other boy was a year or two older than Anil, taller, thick-set, with a broad nose and thick lips. He had only just noticed Anil, and he stood at the edge of the pool, wearing a pair of bathing shorts, waiting for Anil to explain himself.

When Anil didn't say anything, the other called out, 'What are you doing here, mister?'

Anil, who was prepared to be friendly, was surprised at the other's hostility.

'I am swimming,' he replied. 'Why don't you join me?'

'I always swim alone,' said the other. 'This is my pool. I did not invite you to it. And why aren't you wearing any clothes?'

'It is not your business what I wear or do not wear. I have nothing to be ashamed of.'

'You skinny fellow, put on your clothes!'

'Fat fool, take yours off!'

This was too much for the stranger. He strode up to Anil, who still sat on the rock; and planting his broad feet firmly on the sand, said (as though it would settle the matter once and for all), 'Don't you know I am a Punjabi? I do not take insults from villagers like you!'

'So you like to fight with villagers,' said Anil. 'Well, I do not belong to your village. I am a Rajput!'

'I am a Punjabi!'

'I am a Rajput!'

They had reached an impasse. One had said he was a Punjabi, the other had proclaimed himself a Rajput. There was little else that could be said.

'You understand that I am a Punjabi?' repeated the stranger, uneasily aware that the other had not seemed sufficiently impressed.

'I have heard you say it three times,' replied Anil.

'Then why don't you run off?'

'I am waiting for you to run!'

'I shall have to thrash you,' said the Punjabi boy, assuming a violent attitude and showing Anil the palm of his hand.

'Let me see you do it,' said Anil.

'You will see me do it,' said the Punjabi boy.

Anil waited. The other boy made an odd, hissing sound. They stared each other in the eye for almost a minute. Then the Punjabi boy slapped Anil across the face with all his strength. Anil staggered back, feeling giddy. There were thick red finger-marks on his cheek.

'There you are,' exclaimed his assailant. 'Will you be off now?'

By way of reply, Anil swung his arm up and pushed a hard, bony fist into his adversary's face.

And then they were at each other's throats, swaying together on the rock, tumbling on to the sand, rolling over and over, their arms and legs locked in a fierce struggle. Clawing, gasping and cursing, they rolled right into the shallows of the pool.

Even in the water they continued fighting. Sputtering and covered in mud, they groped for each other's heads and throats. But after five minutes of frenzied, unscientific struggle, neither boy had emerged victorious. Their bodies heaving with exhaustion, they stood back from each other, making tremendous efforts to speak.

'So – now do you realise – I am a Punjabi?' gasped the stranger.

'Do you – know I am a Rajput?' said Anil with difficulty.

They gave a moment's consideration to each other's answers, and in that moment of silence there was only their heavy breathing and rapid pounding of their hearts.

'Then you will not leave the pool?' said the Punjabi boy.

'I will not leave it,' said Anil.

'Then we shall have to continue the fight,' said the other.

'All right,' said Anil.

But neither boy moved, neither took the initiative.

Then the Punjabi boy had an inspiration.

'We will continue the fight tomorrow,' he said. 'If you dare to come back tomorrow, we will continue the fight, and I will not let you off as easily as I have done today.'

'I will come tomorrow,' said Anil. 'I will be ready for you.'

They turned their backs on each other, and returning to their respective rocks, dressed, and then left the forest by different routes.

When Anil got home, he found it difficult to account for the cuts and bruises that showed on his face, arms and legs. He could not conceal the fact that he had been in a bad fight, and his mother insisted on his staying home for the rest of the day.

That evening, though, he slipped out of the house and went to the bazaar where he found comfort and solace in a bottle of vividly-coloured lemonade, and a banana-leaf full of hot, sweet jalebis. He had just finished the lemonade when he saw his recent adversary coming down the road.

Anil's first impulse was to turn away and look elsewhere; the second to throw the empty bottle at his enemy; but he did neither of those things. Instead, he stood his ground and scowled at his opponent. And the Punjabi boy said nothing either, but scowled back with equal ferocity.

The next day was as hot as the previous one. Anil felt weak and lazy and not at all eager for a fight. His body was stiff and sore after the previous day's encounter. But he couldn't refuse the challenge. Not to turn up at the pool would be an acknowledgement of defeat. But from the way he was feeling, he know he would be beaten in another fight. Yet he must defy his enemy, outwit him if possible. To surrender now would be to forfeit all rights to the pool in the forest; and he knew it was his pool.

He was half hoping that the Punjabi boy would have forgotten the challenge; but as soon as Anil arrived he saw his opponent stripped to the waist, sitting on a rock at the far end of the pool. The Punjabi boy was rubbing oil on his body, massaging it into his broad thighs. He saw Anil beneath the sal trees, and called a challenge across the water.

'Come over on this side and fight!' he shouted.

But Anil was not going to submit to any conditions laid down by his opponent.

'Come *this* side and fight,' he shouted back defiantly.

'Swim over and fight me here!' called the other. 'Or perhaps you cannot swim the length of this pool!'

Anil could have swum the length of the pool a dozen times without tiring, and in this department he knew he could show the Punjabi boy his superiority. Slipping out of his vest and shorts, he dived straight into the water, cutting through it like a golden fish, and surfacing with hardly a splash. The Punjabi boy's mouth hung open in amazement.

'You can dive!' he exclaimed.

'It is easy,' said Anil, treading water and waiting for another challenge. 'Can't you dive?'

'No,' said the other. 'I jump straight in. But if you will tell me how, I'll make a dive.'

'It is easy,' said Anil. 'Stand straight on the rock, hold your arms out, and allow your head to displace your feet.'

The Punjabi boy stood up, stiff and straight, stretched out his arms, and threw himself at the water. He landed flat on his belly, with a crash that sent the birds screaming out of the trees.

Anil burst into laughter.

'Are you trying to empty the pool?' he asked, as the Punjabi boy came to the surface, spouting water like a small whale.

'Wasn't it good?' asked the boy, evidently proud of his feat.

'Not very good,' said Anil. 'You should have more practice. See, I will do it again!'

And pulling himself up on a rock, he executed another perfect dive. The Punjabi boy waited for him to come up; but, swimming under water, in a world of soft lights and crooked sunshine, Anil circled the boy and came up from behind.

'How did you do that?' asked the astonished youth.

'Can't you swim under water?' asked Anil.

'No, but I will try.'

The Punjabi boy made a tremendous effort to plunge to the bottom of the pool; and, indeed, he thought he had gone right down, though his bottom, like a duck's, remained above the surface.

Anil, however, did not want to sound too discouraging. He was involved in a game of high diplomacy.

'It was not bad,' he said. 'But you need a lot of practice.'

'Will you teach me?' asked his enemy.

'If you like, I will teach you.'

'You must teach me. If you do not teach me, I will

thrash you. Will you come here every day and teach me?'

'If you like,' said Anil. They had pulled themselves out of the water and were sitting side by side on a smooth grey rock.

'My name is Vijay,' said the Punjabi boy. 'What is yours?'

'It is Anil.'

'I am strong, am I not?' said Vijay, bending his arm so that a ball of muscle stood up.

'You are strong,' said Anil. 'You are like a wrestler, a pahlwan.'

'One day I will be Mister Universe!' said Vijay, slapping his thighs, which shook under the impact of his hand.

He looked critically at Anil's hard, thin body. 'You are quite strong yourself,' he conceded, 'but you are too bony. I know, you people do not eat enough. You must come and have your meals with me. I drink one kilo of milk every day. You see, we have got our own cow. Be my friend and I will make you a real pahlwan like me! I know – if you teach me to dive and swim under water, I will make you a pahlwan. This is fair, isn't it?'

'It's fair,' said Anil, though he doubted if he was getting the better of the exchange.

Vijay put his arm around the younger boy's shoulders and said, 'We are friends now, yes?'

They looked at each other with unflinching eyes, and in that moment a friendship was born.

'We are friends,' said Anil.

The birds had settled again in the branches of the sal trees, and the pool was still and limpid in the afternoon shadows. 'It is our pool,' said Vijay. 'Nobody else can come here. Who would dare?'

'Yes, who would dare?' said Anil, smiling with the knowledge that he had won the day.

On the Bench
Stephen Potts

Dear Dad,

Mam's helping me to write this but the words are all mine. Thanks for the football you sent me for my birthday. I practise a lot against next door's wall. I'm not very good yet, but I'm getting better. I'm sorry you couldn't get off work, but it's OK. I hope the army let you off at Christmas. Which isn't long now. Please be careful with your tank and come home soon.

Love, Gary

Dear Dad,

Mam's helping me again but not so much this time. Thank you very much for the new boots. They are great, but I don't wear them to practise against the wall because they need grass, like at the rec. It was good playing there with you and Uncle John. I hope I will be as good as him one day.

Arsenal on Boxing Day was brilliant. I really like that Bergkamp. Is that how you spell it? I jumped and shouted when he got that goal. I wish we could go to every match.

I'm sorry you had to go back to the army early, but Mam says you'll be leaving soon, and it will be better then. I hope so. Maybe when you live with us again you and Mam will not shout so much.

School starts again soon, and I'm glad. The lessons are sometimes fun but the best part is the football in the playground. On Tuesday I can take my new boots because we play in teams in the park.

Love, Gary

Dear Dad,
I saw your car so I left you a note, the traffic warden better not take it away. I haven't seen you for ages. You have to work even harder now you've left the army. I didn't know you worked near here as well. Maybe if you get a chance you could come and watch us play. Our team is quite good now and we won on Saturday. I've got to run after the others. Maybe I'll see you tonight. Can we go to Arsenal again soon?
Love, Gary

Hello? Hello, Dad? I know you're there because you're driving around with your work but Mam said you have a machine to take messages. It's morning break and I'm at the phone in the sweet shop. The money's going quickly so I might not have any left for crisps, but I wanted to say thank you so much for taking me to Highbury again. I hope Bergkamp's going to play again soon. It was good that Uncle John was there. He makes a lot of noise and he's very funny. Will you –
beep beep beep beep beep

Dear Dad,
This is the team sheet for Saturday. Here's my name. I'm supposed to be a wingback, but I don't really know what that is. It's not like the Arsenal programme but I wanted you to have it. I wanted to show you myself, but I had to go to bed because I'm tired after practice, so I'm leaving it with Mam for when you come in. See you Saturday.
Love, Gary

To: s-graham@insAB.com.uk
From: gary@stmark.com.uk

Hello Dad!
This is my first e-mail. We're doing computers now.
I didn't tell you yet. Mam got your e-mail thing but I asked
her not to say until I could use the machine. I checked
with the teacher and she said it's OK. She helped me a lot
too. I hope your boss doesn't mind. There's only one
machine for all the kids, but if you send the e-mail back
the teacher will show it to me. See you tonight.
Gary

Dear Dad,

HAPPY FATHER'S DAY!

I spent ages picking this tie. Mam wanted to choose one
for me but I wouldn't let her. Your suit is dead smart, and
I like it better than the Army clothes, but there's not
enough colours in it. When you put it on, will you show
me how you tie it? You do it so quickly and I can never
work it out.

I'm glad you'll be home all weekend. If the weather's
good, maybe we could all go to the rec again with Uncle
John. I know Mam would like to go to the park and sit by
the pond, but they don't let you play football there, and
the last time we went the ducks bit me, remember.
Anyway, whatever we do will be good.
Love, Gary

Dear Dad,

Here is my school report. Miss Johnson said I had to show it to you and Mam so you could talk about it at the meeting next week. It's not bad, I think, except for what Mr Rigby said. I don't know what mischief means, and whatever he tells you I did, I didn't. He doesn't like any of us and we don't like him. Maybe that's why he gives us all bad reports.

I don't know what's wrong with Mam. She's gone all quiet and doesn't laugh. I think it's because you didn't come with her and me to the park after we played football. I was scared but the ducks were OK. Mam laughed at me when the ducks came up for bread, but she stopped laughing when I said I kept seeing your car near our practice place. Please will you talk to her and find out what's wrong?

Love, Gary

Dear Dad,

I'm taking this to your work because you don't come home now. I was going to post it but I don't know where you live and I didn't want to ask Mam. I'm going to borrow Jimmy's bike at break and bring it there myself. I hope I will see you, but I think you'll be out in your car.

I don't know what Mr Rigby told you but you're so angry with me, and Mam doesn't talk since the teachers' night, so it must have been bad. Then you and Mam shouted so much I got scared. The glass in the door cracked when you shut it so hard. I could hear it upstairs, and I could hear Mam crying, but she wouldn't tell me why. I asked her what Mr Rigby told you, but she said she didn't know, you only came for the end part of the meeting and Mr Rigby had gone. I don't know what I've done wrong, so I can't make it right. If you can't come

home and tell me please come to practice tomorrow. I can stay after for a while. But please don't be angry.
Love, Gary

Dear Dad,
Your secretary lady was very nice to me when I brought the letter to your work, and she showed me how to write the envelope to where you live now, but I don't know why she came with you to watch us play. Does she like football? I said to Mam you were there. She went sad again, and asked if you were on your own. I said no and made her cry. I'm glad you are not angry with me now, but I don't think you should be angry with Mam.

We're playing again on Saturday. I would like it if you could come but please don't bring that lady.
Love, Gary

Dear Dad,
Thank you for putting the Arsenal ticket through the door. I didn't get it till after the match because Uncle John and Aunty Pat took Mam and me to the seaside for the whole weekend. It was great. I sent you a postcard but you'll get this first. Uncle John and me went in a boat and we fished off the pier and we played football on the beach. Mam and Aunty Pat sat in deckchairs and talked and talked. When we got back from the boat Mam's eyes were red but she was laughing like she hasn't done for a long time. She bought us all fish and chips after.

We're playing in the semi-final soon, and I hope you will come. Uncle John showed me how to bend the ball, like at free kicks. Maybe I will get a chance to show you.
Love, Gary

Dear Dad,

It's not as sunny as on the picture but it's good fun all the same. We're sitting at the bottom of the cliff, where I put the cross, like in spot-the-ball. Uncle John and me are going in a boat soon, round to the rocks at the edge of the picture. We've already been fishing on the pier but I didn't catch anything. Maybe I will, on the boat.

Mam's talking with Aunty Pat. She doesn't know I'm sending this. Will you take her to the pictures on her birthday, like you did last year?

Love, Gary

Dear Dad,

I'm glad you came to watch us and sorry that when I did the free kick it wouldn't bend. It does when I practise, honest. The final is in two weeks. We practise every day now, and the whole school's really excited. All the girls want to talk to us. It's funny, they never talked to me before.

Thank you for not bringing that secretary lady. I didn't want to meet her after, like you said, because I had to get back for tea. Uncle John and Aunty Pat were coming round and Mam said not to be late. Uncle John said he'd take me to Arsenal Saturday. Mam surprised us all when she said she wanted to come too. She said that's all she wants for her birthday this year, but I'm going to get her another book about making bracelets and things. She's started doing that again and she sold some at the car boot sale on Sunday. She bought me a Bergkamp shirt with the money.

I didn't like it when you said that lady was my new mam. I hope you don't call her that when I'm not there. I won't tell Mam you said it, and maybe it's best if you don't come to Arsenal with us.

Love, Gary

Dad? Are you there? Hello? I'll just talk to your machine. The Arsenal game was good. Mam loved it. She shouts even more than me. Was it OK for you watching it on TV? When you came to watch us practise yesterday the teachers were really rushing us back to school, so I didn't get time to talk to you enough. I've thought about what you said, about bringing that lady to watch us in the final. Well I don't want her to come. Mam and Aunty Pat and Uncle John will be there. If you're going to bring that lady with you I don't want you to come. I want—
beep beep beep beepbeeeeeeeeep

She

Rosa Guy

'Just where do you think you're going?' she said.

'To the bathroom,' I said.

'No, you're not,' she said. 'Not before you wash up these dishes.'

'This is a matter of urgent necessity,' I said. I hated that even my going to the bathroom had to be questioned.

'Don't want to hear,' she said. 'I'm sick and tired of emergency, emergency every night after dinner. Get to that sink.'

'I'll wash the dishes,' Linda said. She got up and started to clear off the table. I slipped out of the kitchen. The angry voice followed me down the hall:

'Linda, don't keep letting your sister get away with everything.'

'I don't mind – really, Dorine,' Linda said.

'That girl's just too damn lazy…' I shut the bathroom door to muffle the sounds of her grievances against me. She didn't like me. She never had. And I didn't care. Stepmothers…!

Searching the bottom of the hamper for the science fiction magazine I had hidden beneath the dirty clothes, I sat on the toilet and began to read to get out of this world – as far from her as I could get.

From the day she had walked into our house she'd been on to me. I was lying on my bed reading when she and Daddy pushed into my room without knocking. Our eyes locked. She didn't speak. Neither did I.

I was in a panic. Daddy had forbidden me to read fairy tales. 'At twelve years old! You're too old,' he'd said. He wanted me to read only school books. I hadn't had time to hide the book of fairy tales beneath my mattress as I usually did. I curled up around it, praying to keep his eyes from it.

But Daddy was only showing her the apartment. So she had to turn to inspect my almost bare room. When she looked back at me, her eyes said: What are you doing reading in this miserable room instead of doing something useful around this terrible house? My eyes answered: What's it to you?

They left the room the way they'd come. Abruptly. Hearing their footsteps going towards the kitchen, I got up and followed. Linda was in the kitchen, washing fish for our dinner. When they went in, Linda looked up and smiled.

'What a lovely girl,' Dorine said, and the shock of her American accent went right through me. What was Daddy doing with an American woman! 'She's got to be the prettiest child I ever did see. My name is Dorine,' she said.

From the first she had chosen Linda over me. Maybe because Linda was pretty, with her long, thick hair and clear brown eyes and brown velvet skin. I was plain-looking. Or maybe because Linda was two years older – already a teenager.

'You're Daddy's friend,' Linda said, batting her long black eyelashes the way she always did whenever someone paid her a compliment. 'I didn't know Daddy had a lady friend.' Daddy gave Linda a quick look and she changed to: 'My name is Linda. And that's – ' she pointed to where I stood in the doorway – 'the baby. Her name is Gogi.'

But Dorine had already turned away from Linda to inspect the kitchen. And suddenly I saw our kitchen and the sweat of embarrassment almost drowned me: the sink was leaking and had a pan under it to catch the dirty water; the windowpanes were broken and stuffed with newspapers to keep out winter; the linoleum was worn, showing the soft wood beneath.

And she wore furs. Our mother had never worn furs. Not even when Daddy had had lots of money. People from the tropics didn't think of wearing things like furs. And the way Dorine looked around – nose squinched up, mouth pulled back – judging us, West Indians.

Daddy stood in the middle of the kitchen, quieter than usual – big, broad, handsome in his black overcoat, around his arm the black crepe band of mourning. His hands were deep in the pockets of his grey wool suit. And she hit out at him: 'Damn, Harry, how can you live like this!'

Linda stopped smiling then. Daddy's eyebrows quivered. My mouth got tight with satisfaction. Daddy had a mean temper. I waited for him to blast her out of our house and out of our lives. She had socked us where we hurt – our pride.

'How you mean?' Daddy had said. 'We ain't live so. You see mi restaurant...' So, he had known her while our mother was still alive. '...I lose it,' he said. 'Mi wife dead. I sell me house, mi furniture, mi car. I— I— mi friend let me stay here for a time – but only for a short time.' He was begging! I hated that he stood there begging.

'If it's only one minute, that's one minute too damn long,' she said.

Lifting my head from the science fiction magazine to turn a page, I heard the sound of pots banging against pans in the kitchen. And I heard Dorine's footsteps in the hall. I waited for the knob to turn on the bathroom door. She sometimes did that. But this time she went on into the living room. A short time later I heard the television playing.

It had been two years since the pointing, the ordering, the arranging and rearranging of our lives had begun. She had forced us to leave our old free apartment and move into her big one with its big rooms, its big kitchen and all those dozens of pots and pans for all things and all occasions. We had to listen to her constant: 'Cleanliness is next to godliness', and 'A good housekeeper has a place for everything and keeps everything in its place'. Like who told her that what we wanted most in life was to be housekeepers? I didn't!

Daddy let her get away with everything. He stayed out most days looking for work. And he spent evenings gambling with his friends. The times he spent at home he spent with her – laughing and joking in their bedroom. She entertained him to keep him there. I'd seen her flashing around the house in her peach-coloured satin dressing gown, her feet pushed into peach-coloured frilly mules, her big white teeth showing all across her face, her gown falling away to expose plump brown knees. Guess that's what he liked – that combination of peach satin and smooth brown skin.

She worked, a singer. Sometimes for weeks she'd been out on the road. Then she'd come home with her friends and they'd do all that loud American talking and laughing. She sometimes brought us lovely things back from 'the road'. Blouses, underwear, coats. She won Linda's affection like that and might have won mine if I hadn't heard a man friend say to her one day: 'Dorine, it's bad enough you got yourself hooked up with that West Indian. But how did you manage to get in a family way?'

'Big Red,' she called him. 'I'm in love.'

'With all of 'em?' he asked.

'They come with the deal,' she said.

'Some deal,' he answered.

'You don't need to worry none, Big Red,' she said. 'They earn their keep.'

She saw me standing in the doorway then, and her big eyes stretched out almost to where I stood. Guilty. Her mouth opened. I walked away. I had heard enough. I went right in and told Linda. 'That's what she wants us around for,' I said. 'To be her maids.'

'Gogi,' Linda said. 'She probably didn't mean it that way at all.'

'What other way could she mean it?' I asked. Innocent Linda. She never saw the evil in the hearts and minds of people.

But from that day Dorine picked on me. When I vacuumed the hall, she called me to show me specks I could hardly see and made me vacuum over again. When I cleaned my room, she went in and ran her fingers over the woodwork to show me how much dust I had left behind. 'That ain't the way we do things around here,' she liked to say. 'Do it right or don't do it at all.' As though I had a choice!

'Trying to work me to death, that's what she's doing,' I complained to Linda.

'But why don't you do things right the first time, Gogi?' Linda said. I could only stare at her. My sister!

We had always been close. Linda hadn't minded doing things for me before Dorine came, as long as I read to her. Linda never had time for things like reading. She knew she was pretty and kept trying to make herself perfect. Linda washed her blouses and underwear by hand. She ironed her clothes to defeat even the thought of a wrinkle. And she had always done mine along with hers, just to have me read to her.

But now our stepmother who had turned our father against us had turned my sister against me! Well, if Linda wanted to be a maid, that was her business. I did enough when I vacuumed the hall and cleaned my room. If Linda had to take Dorine's side against me, then let Dorine read for her. I was satisfied to do my reading to myself – by myself.

Sitting too long on the toilet, I felt the seat cut into my thighs. I got up to unstick myself and leaving the toilet unflushed – not to give away that I had finished – I sat on the closed stool, listening to what ought to have been sounds of glass clinking against glass, of china against china.

The quiet outside the bathroom unsettled me. I usually knew when Linda had finished with the dishes. I always heard when she passed to join Dorine in the living room. They played the television loud, thinking to make me jealous, making me feel unneeded, pretending not to care that I had shut myself from them and that I might go to my room without even a goodnight. But I hadn't heard Linda pass!

The television kept playing. I strained to hear the programme to tell the time. It was on too low. Getting up, I thought of going out to see how things were but sat down again. Better to give Linda a little more time. I started another story.

I had only half finished when my concentration snapped. The television had been turned off. I tried to but couldn't get back into the story. Instead I sat listening, hoping to pick up sounds from the silent house. What time was it?

Getting up, I put my ear to the door. No outside sound. Unlocking the door, I cracked it open and peeked out. The hallway was dark! Everybody had gone to bed! How late was it? Taking off my shoes I started tiptoeing down towards my room. Then from the dark behind me I heard: 'Ain't no sense in all that creeping. Them dishes waiting ain't got no ears.' I spun around. A light went on and there she was, lying on a chaise longue that had been pulled up to the living room door. 'That's right, it's me,' she said. 'And it's one o'clock in the morning. Which gives you enough time to wash every dish in the sink squeaking clean before one o'clock noon.'

Tears popped into my eyes as she marched me down past my room where Linda slept, into the kitchen. Tears kept washing my cheeks as I washed dishes. She sat inspecting every one, acting as though we were playing games. If we were, I expected it to go on forever. She had tricked me – and she had won.

Who's Afraid?
Philippa Pearce

'Will my cousin Dicky be there?'

'Everyone's been asked. Cousins, aunts, uncles, great-aunts, great-uncles – the lot. I've told you: it's your great-grandmother's hundredth birthday party.'

'But will Dicky Hutt be there?'

'I'm sure he will be.'

'Anyway, Joe, why do you want to know?'

Joe's mother and father were staring at Joe; and Joe said, 'I hate Dicky.'

'Now, Joe!' said his mother; and his father asked: 'Why on earth do you hate Dicky?'

'I just do,' said Joe. He turned away, to end the conversation; but inside his head he was saying: 'I'd like to kill Dicky Hutt. Before he tries to kill me.'

When the day of the birthday came, everyone – just as Joe's mother had said – was there. Relations of all ages swarmed over the little house where Great-grandmother lived, looked after by Great-aunt Madge. Fortunately, Great-grandmother had been born in the summer, and now – a hundred years later – the sun shone warmly on her celebrations. Great-aunt Madge shooed everyone into the garden for the photograph. The grown-ups sat on chairs, or stood in rows, and the children sat cross-legged in a row in the very front. (At one end, Joe; at the other, Dicky; and Dicky's stare at Joe said: 'If I catch you, I'll kill you…') There was a gap in the centre of this front row for a table with the tiered birthday cake and its hundred candles.

And behind the cake sat Great-grandmother in her wheel-chair, with one shawl over her knees and another round her shoulders. Great-aunt Madge stood just behind her.

Great-grandmother faced the camera with a steady gaze from eyes that saw nothing by now – she had become blind in old age. Whether she heard much was doubtful. Certainly, she never spoke or turned her head even a fraction as if to listen.

After the photograph and the cutting of the cake, the grown-ups stood around drinking tea and talking. (Great-grandmother had been wheeled off somewhere indoors for a rest.) The children, if they were very young, clung to their parents; the older ones sidled about aimlessly – aimlessly, except that Joe could see Dicky always sidling towards him, staring his hatred. So Joe sidled away and sidled away...

'Children!' cried Great-aunt Madge. 'What about a good old game? What about hide-and-seek? There's the garden to hide in, and most of the house.'

Some of the children still clung to their parents; others said 'yes' to hide-and-seek. Dicky Hutt said 'yes'. Joe said 'no'; but his father said impatiently: 'Don't be soft! Go off and play with the others.'

Dicky Hutt shouted: 'I'll be He!' So he was. Dicky Hutt shut his eyes and began to count at once. When he had counted a hundred, he would open his eyes and begin to search.

Joe knew who he would search for with the bitterest thoroughness: himself.

Joe was afraid – too afraid to think well. He thought at first that he would hide in the garden, where there were at least grown-ups about – but then he didn't trust Dicky not to be secretly watching under his eyelashes, to see exactly where he went. Joe couldn't bear the thought of that.

So, after all, he went indoors to hide; but by then some of the best hiding-places had been taken. And out in the garden Dicky Hutt was counting fast, shouting aloud his total at every count of ten. 'Seventy!' he was shouting now; and Joe had just looked behind the sofa in the front room, and there was already someone crouching there. And there was also someone hiding under the pile of visitors' coats – 'Eighty!' came Dicky Hutt's voice from the garden – and two children already in the stair cupboard, when he thought of that hiding-place. So he must go on looking for somewhere – anywhere – to hide – and 'Ninety!' from outside – *anywhere* to hide – and for the second time he came to the door with the notice pinned to it that said: 'Keep out! Signed: Madge.'

'A hundred! I'm coming!' shouted Dicky Hutt. And Joe turned the handle of the forbidden door and slipped inside and shut the door behind him.

The room was very dim, because the curtains had been drawn close; and its quietness seemed empty. But Joe's eyes began to be able to pick out the furnishings of the room, even in the half-light; table, chair, roll-top desk, and also – like just another piece of furniture, and just as immobile – Great-grandmother's wheelchair and Great-grandmother sitting in it.

He stood, she sat, both silent, still; and Dicky Hutt's thundering footsteps and voice were outside, passing the door, and then far away.

He thought she did not know that he had come into her room; but a low, slow voice reached him: 'Who's there?'

He whispered: 'It's only me – Joe.'

Silence; and then the low, slow voice again: 'Who's there?'

He was moving towards her, to speak in her very ear, when she spoke a third time: 'Who's there?'

And this time he heard in her voice the little tremble of fear: he recognised it. He came to her chair, and laid his hand on hers. For a second he felt her weakly pull away, and then she let his hand rest, but turned her own, so that his hand fell into hers. She held his hand, fingered it slowly. He wanted her to know that he meant her no harm; he wanted her to say: 'This is a small hand, a child's hand. You are only a child, after all.'

But she did not speak again.

He stood there; she sat there; and the excited screams and laughter and running footsteps of hide-and-seek were very far away.

At last, Joe could tell from the sounds outside that the game of hide-and-seek was nearly over. He must be the last player not to be found and chased by Dicky Hutt. For now Dicky Hutt was wandering about, calling, 'Come out, Joe! I know where you're hiding, Joe, so you might as well come out! I shall find you, Joe – I shall find you!'

The roving footsteps passed the forbidden doorway several times; but – no, this time they did not pass. Dicky Hutt had stopped outside.

The silence outside the door made Joe tremble: he tried to stop trembling, for the sake of the hand that held his, but he could not. He felt that old, old skin-and-bony hand close on his, as if questioning what was happening, what was wrong.

But he had no voice to explain to her. He had no voice at all.

His eyes were on the knob of the door. Even through the gloom he could see that it was turning. Then the door was creeping open – not fast, but steadily; not far, but far enough—

It opened far enough for Dicky Hutt to slip through. He stood there, inside the dim room. Joe could see his bulk there: Dicky Hutt had always been bigger than he was; now he loomed huge. And he was staring directly at Joe.

Joe's whole body was shaking. He felt as if he were shaking to pieces. He wished that he could.

His great-grandmother held his shaking hand in hers.

Dicky Hutt took a step forward into the room.

Joe had no hope. He felt his great-grandmother lean forward a little in her chair, tautening her grip on his hand as she did so. In her low, slow voice she was saying: 'Who—' And Joe thought, He won't bother to answer her; he'll just come for me. He'll *come* for me...

But the low, slow voice went on: 'Whooooooooooo—' She was hooting like some ghost-throated owl; and then the hooting raised itself into a thin, eerie wailing. Next, through the wailing, she began to gibber, with effect so startling – so horrifying – that Joe forgot Dicky Hutt for a moment, and turned to look at her. His great-grandmother's mouth was partly open, and she was making her false teeth do a kind of devil's dance inside it.

And when Joe looked towards Dicky Hutt again, he had gone. The door was closing, the knob turning. The door clicked shut, and Joe could hear Dicky Hutt's feet tiptoeing away.

When Joe looked at his great-grandmother again, she was sitting back in her chair. Her mouth was closed; the gibbering and the hooting and the wailing had ceased. She looked exhausted – or had she died? But no, she was just looking unbelievably old.

He did not disturb her. He stood by the chair some time longer. Then he heard his parents calling over the house for him: they wanted to go home.

He moved his hand out of hers – the grasp was slack now: perhaps she had fallen asleep. He thought he wanted to kiss her goodbye; but then he did not want the feel of that century-old cheek against his lips.

So he simply slipped away from her and out of the room.

He never saw her again. Nearly a year later, at home, the news came of her death. Joe's mother said: 'Poor old thing...'

Joe's father (whose grandmother Great-grandmother had been) said, 'When I was a little boy, she was fun. I remember her. Jokey, then; full of tricks...'

Joe's mother said, 'Well, she'd outlived all that. Outlived everything. Too old to be any use to herself – or to anyone else. A burden, only.'

Joe said nothing; but he wished now that he had kissed her cheek, to say goodbye, and to thank her.

A Game of Cards
Witi Ihimaera

The train pulled into the station. For a moment there was confusion: a voice blaring over the loudspeaker system, people getting off the train, the bustling and shoving of the crowd on the platform.

And there was Dad, waiting for me. We hugged each other. We hadn't seen each other for a long time. Then we kissed. But I could tell something was wrong.

'Your Nanny Miro,' he said. 'She's very sick.'

Nanny Miro... among all my nannies, she was the one I loved most. Everybody used to say I was her favourite mokopuna*, and that she loved me more than her own children who'd grown up and had kids of their own.

She lived down the road from us, right next to the meeting house in the big old homestead which everybody in the village called 'The Museum' because it housed the prized possessions of the whanau, the village family. Because she was rich and had a lot of land, we all used to wonder why Nanny Miro didn't buy a newer, more modern house. But Nanny didn't want to move. She liked her own house just as it was.

'Anyway,' she used to say, 'what with all my haddit* kids and their haddit kids and all this haddit whanau* being broke all the time and coming to ask me for some money, how can I afford to buy a new house?'

Nanny didn't really care about money though. 'Who needs it?' she used to say. 'What do you think I had all these kids for, ay? To look after me, I'm not dumb!'

---

mokopuna: grand-child (including great niece and great nephew)
haddit: no-good
whanau: the village family

Then she would cackle to herself. But it wasn't true really, because her family would send all their kids to her place when they were broke and she looked after them! She liked her mokopunas, but not for too long. She'd ring up their parents and say:

'Hey! When you coming to pick up your hoha* kids! They're wrecking the place!'

Yet, always, when they left, she would have a little weep, and give them some money.

I used to like going to Nanny's place. For me it was a big treasure house, glistening with sports trophies and photographs, pieces of carvings and greenstone, and feather cloaks* hanging from the walls.

Most times, a lot of women would be there playing cards with Nanny. Nanny loved all card games – five hundred, poker, canasta, pontoon, whist, euchre – you name it, she could play it.

I liked sitting and watching them. Mrs Heta would always be there, and when it came to cards she was both Nanny's best friend and worst enemy. And the two of them were the biggest cheats I ever saw.

Mrs Heta would cough and reach for a hanky while slyly slipping a card from beneath her dress. And she was always reneging* in five hundred! But her greatest asset was her eyes, which were big and googly. One eye would look straight ahead, while the other swivelled around, having a look at the cards in the hands of the women sitting next to her.

'Eeee! You cheat!' Nanny would say. 'You just keep your eyes to yourself, Maka tiko bum!*'

---

hoha: wearisome
feather cloaks: traditional Maori garments
reneging: changing her mind
tiko bum: fat bum

Mrs Heta would look at Nanny as if she were offended. Then she would sniff and say: 'You the cheat yourself, Miro Mananui. I saw you sneaking that ace from the bottom of the pack.'

'How do you know I got an ace Maka?' Nanny would say. 'I know you! You dealt this hand, and you stuck that ace down there for yourself, you cheat! Well, ana*! I got it now! So take that!'

And she would slap down her hand.

'Sweet, ay?' she would laugh. 'Good, Kapai lalelale?*' And she would sometimes wiggle her hips, making her victory sweeter.

'Eeee! Miro!' Mrs Heta would say. 'Well, I got a good hand too!'

And she would slap her hand down and bellow with laughter.

'Take that!'

And always, they would squabble. I often wondered how they ever remained friends. The names they called each other!

Sometimes, I would go and see Nanny and she would be all alone, playing patience. If there was nobody to play with her, she'd always play patience. And still she cheated! I'd see her hands fumbling across the cards, turning up a jack or queen she needed, and then she'd laugh and say:

'I'm too good for this game!'

She used to try to teach me some of the games, but I wasn't very interested, and I didn't yell and shout at her like the women did. She liked the bickering.

'Aue*…' she would sigh. Then she'd look at me and

---

ana: come on
Kapai lalelale: very good
aue: alas

begin dealing out the cards in the only game I ever knew how to play.

And we would yell snap! all the afternoon.

Now, Nanny was sick.

I went to see her that afternoon after I'd dropped my suitcases at home. Nanny Tama, her husband, opened the door. We embraced and he began to weep on my shoulder.

'Your Nanny Miro,' he whispered. 'She's… she's…'

He couldn't say the words. He motioned me to her bedroom.

Nanny Miro was lying in bed. And she was so old looking. Her face was very grey, and she looked like a tiny wrinkled doll in that big bed. She was so thin now, and seemed all bones.

I walked into the room. She was asleep. I sat down on the bed beside her, and looked at her lovingly.

Even when I was a child, she must have been old. But I'd never realised it. She must have been over seventy now. Why do people you love grow old so suddenly?

The room had a strange, antiseptic smell. Underneath the bed was a big chamber pot, yellow with urine. And the pillow was flecked with small spots of blood where she had been coughing.

I shook her gently.

'Nanny… Nanny, wake up.'

She moaned. A long, hoarse sigh grew on her lips. Her eyelids fluttered, and she looked at me with blank eyes… and then tears began to roll down her cheeks.

'Don't cry, Nanny,' I said. 'Don't cry. I'm here.'

But she wouldn't stop.

So I sat beside her on the bed and she lifted her hands to me.

'Haere mai*, mokopuna. Haere mai. Mmm. Mmm.'

And I bent within her arms and we pressed noses*.

After a while, she calmed down. She seemed to be her own self.

'What a haddit mokopuna you are,' she wept. 'It's only when I'm just about in my grave that you come to see me.'

'I couldn't see you last time I was home,' I explained. 'I was too busy.'

'Yes, I know you fullas,' she grumbled. 'It's only when I'm almost dead that you come for some money.'

'I don't want your money, Nanny.'

'What's wrong with my money!' she said. 'Nothing's wrong with it! Don't you want any?'

'Of course I do,' I laughed. 'But I know you! I bet you lost it all on poker!'

She giggled. Then she was my Nanny again. The Nanny I knew.

We talked for a long time. I told her about what I was doing in Wellington and all the neat girls who were after me.

'You teka!*' she giggled. 'Who'd want to have you!'

And she showed me all her injection needles and pills and told me how she'd wanted to come home from the hospital, so they'd let her.

'You know why I wanted to come home?' she asked. 'I didn't like all those strange nurses looking at my bum when they gave me those injections. I was so sick, mokopuna, I couldn't even go to the lav, and I'd rather wet my own bed not their neat bed. That's why I come home.'

---

haere mai: welcome, come
pressed noses: a loving greeting, like a kiss
teka: to tell lies

Afterwards, I played the piano for Nanny. She used to like *Me He Manurere* so I played it for her, and I could hear her quavering voice singing in her room.

Me he manurere aue…

When I finally left Nanny I told her I would come back in the morning.

But that night, Nanny Tama rang up.

'Your Nanny Miro, she's dying.'

We all rushed to Nanny's house. It was already crowded. All the old women were there. Nanny was lying very still. Then she looked up and whispered to Mrs Heta:

'Maka … Maka tiko bum … I want a game of cards…'

A pack of cards was found. The old ladies sat round the bed, playing. Everybody else decided to play cards too, to keep Nanny company. The men played poker in the kitchen and sitting room. The kids played snap in the other bedrooms. The house overflowed with card players, even onto the lawn outside Nanny's window, where she could see.

The women laid the cards out on the bed. They dealt the first hand. They cackled and joked with Nanny, trying not to cry. And Mrs Heta kept saying to Nanny:

'Eee! You cheat Miro. You cheat!' And she made her googly eye reach far over to see Nanny's cards.

'You think you can see, ay, Maka tiko bum?' Nanny coughed. 'You think you're going to win this hand, ay? Well, take that!'

She slammed down a full house.

The other women goggled at the cards. Mrs Heta looked at her own cards. Then she smiled through her tears and yelled:

'Eee! You cheat Miro! I got two aces in my hand already! Only four in the pack. So how come you got three aces in your hand?'

Everybody laughed. Nanny and Mrs Heta started

squabbling as they always did, pointing at each other and saying: 'You cheat, not me!' And Nanny Miro said: 'I saw you, Maka tiko bum, I saw you sneaking that card from under the blanket.'

She began to laugh. Quietly. Her eyes streaming with tears.

And while she was laughing, she died.

Everybody was silent. Then Mrs Heta took the cards from Nanny's hands and kissed her.

'You the cheat, Miro,' she whispered. 'You the cheat yourself...'

We buried Nanny on the hill with the rest of her family. During her tangi*, Mrs Heta played patience with Nanny, spreading the cards across the casket.

Later in the year, Mrs Heta, she died too. She was buried right next to Nanny, so that they could keep on playing cards.

And I bet you they're still squabbling up there...

'Eee! You cheat Miro...'

'You the cheat, Maka tiko bum. You, you the cheat...'

---

*tangi: funeral, lasting three days

Baby X
Anon

Once upon a time a baby named X was born. This baby was named X so that nobody could tell whether it was a boy or a girl. Its parents could tell of course but they couldn't tell anybody else. They couldn't even tell Baby X at first.

You see, it was all part of a very important, secret scientific Xperiment known officially as Project Baby X.

Long before Baby X was born a lot of scientists had to be paid to work out the details of the Xperiment and to write the Official Instructions Manual for Baby X's parents and most important of all to find the right set of parents to bring up Baby X.

But finally the scientists found the Joneses, who really wanted to raise an X more than any other kind of baby, no matter how much trouble it would be. Ms and Mr Jones had to promise that they would take equal turns caring for X and feeding it and singing lullabies.

The day the Joneses brought their baby home lots of friends and relatives came over to see it. None of them knew about the secret Xperiment though. When the Joneses smiled and said, 'It's an X,' nobody knew what to say. They couldn't say 'Look at her cute little dimples' and they couldn't say 'Look how strong his muscles are' and they couldn't say just plain 'kitchy coo'. In fact they all thought the Joneses were playing some kind of rude joke.

But of course, the Joneses were not joking. 'It's an X' was absolutely all they would say, and that made the friends and relatives very angry. The relatives all felt very embarrassed about having an X in the family. 'People will think there's something wrong with it' some of them whispered. 'There is something wrong with it,' others whispered back.

'Nonsense' the Joneses told them cheerfully. 'What could possibly be wrong with this perfectly adorable X? Nobody could answer that except Baby X who had just finished its bottle. Baby X's answer was a loud satisfied burp!

Clearly, nothing at all was wrong. Nevertheless, none of the relatives felt comfortable about buying a present for Baby X. The cousins who sent the baby a tiny pair of boxing gloves would not come and visit anymore, and the neighbours who sent a pink flowered romper suit drew their curtains when the Joneses passed their house.

Ms and Mr Jones had to be Xtra careful about how they played with little X. They knew that if they kept bouncing it in the air and saying how strong and active it was they'd be treating it more like a boy than an X. But if all they did was cuddle it and kiss it and tell it how sweet and dainty it was, they'd be treating it more like a girl than an X. On page 1654 of the Official Instructions Manual the scientists prescribed 'plenty of bouncing and plenty of cuddling both'. X ought to be strong and sweet and active – forget about the dainty altogether.

Meanwhile the Joneses were worrying about other problems. Toys, for instance. And clothes. Mr Jones wandered helplessly up and down the aisles finding out what X needed. But everything in the store was piled up in sections marked 'Boys' or 'Girls'. There were 'Boy's pyjamas' and 'Girl's underwear' and 'Boy's fire engines' and 'Girl's housekeeping sets.' Mr Jones went home without buying anything for X. That night, he and Ms Jones consulted page 2326 of the Official Instructions Manual. 'Buy plenty of everything' it said firmly. So they bought plenty of sturdy blue pyjamas in the Boys department and cheerful flowered underwear in the Girls department and they bought all kinds of toys. A boy doll that made pee-pee and cried Papa, and a girl doll that talked in three languages and said 'I am the president of General Motors'. They also bought a story book about a brave princess who rescued a handsome prince from his ivory tower and another one about a sister and brother who grew up to be a baseball star and a ballet star and you had to guess which was which.

By the time X grew big enough to play with other children the Joneses' trouble had grown bigger too. Once a little girl grabbed X's shovel in the sandbox and zonked X on the head with it. 'Now Tracy', the little girl's mother scolded. 'Little girls mustn't hit little…' and she turned to ask X, 'Are you a boy or a girl dear?' Mr Jones who was sitting near held his breath. X smiled and even though its head had never been zonked so hard before, replied 'I'm an X'. 'You're a what?' exclaimed the lady. 'You're a little brat, you mean.' 'But little girls mustn't hit little X's either,' said X retrieving the shovel and smiling again. 'What good does hitting do anyway?' X's father grinned at X. At their next secret Project X meeting the scientists grinned and said Baby X was doing fine.

But it was then time for X to start school. The Joneses were really worried about this because school was even more full of rules for boys and girls, and there were no rules for X's. The teacher would tell boys to form one line and girls to form another. There would be boys' games and girls' games and boys' secrets and girls' secrets. The school library would have a list of recommended books for boys and another for girls. Pretty soon boys and girls would hardly talk to each other. What would happen to poor little X?

The Joneses had asked X's teacher if the class could line up alphabetically instead of boys and girls, and if X could use the principal's bathroom as it wasn't marked Boy or Girl. X's teacher promised to take care of all these problems: but no one could help with X's biggest problem, 'Other Children'.

After school X wanted to play with Other Children. 'How about football?' it asked the girls. They giggled. 'How about weaving baskets?' it asked the boys. They giggled too and made faces. That night Ms and Mr Jones asked how things had gone at school. X said sadly the lessons were OK but otherwise school was a terrible place for an X – it seemed as if Other Children never wanted an X for a friend.

Once more, the Joneses read the Official Instructions Manual. Under 'Other Children' they found the message 'What do you expect? Other Children have to obey all the silly boy and girl rules because their parents taught them to. Lucky X, you don't have to stick to rules at all. All you do is be yourself. PS We're not saying it will be easy.'

X liked being itself. But X cried a lot that night partly because it felt afraid. So X's father held X tight and cuddled it and couldn't help crying too. And X's Mother cheered them both up by reading an Xciting story about an enchanted prince called Sleeping Handsome who woke up when Princess Charming kissed him. The next morning they all felt much better and little X went back to school with a brave smile.

There was a relay race in the gym, and a baking contest and X won the relay race and almost won the baking contest Xcept it forgot to light the oven, which only proves that nobody is perfect.

One of the Other Children noticed something else. 'Winning or losing doesn't seem to matter to X. X seems to have fun at boy and girl skills.'

'Come to think of it' said another child, 'Maybe X is having twice the fun we are.' So after school that day, the girl who won the baking contest gave X a big slice of cake and the boy who nearly won the race asked X to race him home. From then on some funny things happened. Susie, who sat next to X, refused to wear pink dresses to school anymore. She wanted to wear red and white check overalls like X's, they were better for climbing monkey bars. Then Jim, the class football nut, started wheeling his sister's doll's pram round the football field. He'd put on his football uniform except the helmet. Then he put the helmet in the pram lovingly tucked under a set of shoulder pads. Then he'd push it round the football field singing 'Rockabye baby' to his helmet. He told his family X did the same thing so it must be OK, after all, X was now the team's quarterback.

Susie's parents were horrified by her behaviour and Jim's were worried sick about him. But the worst came when the twins Joe and Peggy decided to share everything with each other. Peggy used Joe's hockey skates and his microscope and shared his newspaper round. Joe used Peggy's needlework kit and cookbooks and took three of her baby-sitting jobs. Peggy used the lawnmower and Joe the vacuum cleaner.

Their parents weren't one bit pleased with Peggy's wonderful chemistry experiments or with Joe's embroidered pillows. They didn't care that Peggy mowed the lawn better and that Joe vacuumed the carpet better. In fact they were furious. 'It's all that little X's fault' they agreed. 'Just because X doesn't know what it is, or what it's supposed to be, it wants to get everyone mixed up too.' Peggy and Joe were forbidden to play with X. So was Susie and then Jim and then all the Other Children. But it was too late. The Other Children stayed mixed up and happy and free and refused to go back to the way they had been before.

Finally Joe and Peggy's parents decided to call an

emergency meeting of the Parent Teacher Association, in order to discuss the X problem. They sent a report to the principal saying X was a disruptive influence. They wanted immediate action. The Joneses, they said, should be forced to tell whether X was a boy or a girl, and then X should be forced to behave like whichever it was. If the Joneses refused to say, the Parent Teacher Association said X must have an Xamination. The school doctor should examine X and issue a report.

At exactly 9 o'clock the next day X reported to the school surgery. The principal, the Parent Teacher Association, teachers, classmates and Ms and Mr Jones waited outside.

Nobody knew the details of the test X was to be given but everybody knew it would be very hard and that it would reveal exactly what everyone wanted to know about X but were afraid to ask.

At last the door opened. Everyone crowded round to hear the results. X didn't look any different; in fact X smiled. But the doctor looked terrible as if he was crying. 'What happened?' everyone shouted. Had X done something disgraceful? 'Wouldn't be surprised' said Peggy and Joe's parents. 'Did X flunk the whole test?' cried Susie's parents. 'Or just most of it?' yelled Jim's parents. 'Oh dear', sighed Ms and Mr Jones. 'Sssh' said the principal, 'the doctor is trying to speak'. Wiping his eyes and clearing his throat, the doctor began in a hoarse whisper. 'In my opinion' he whispered 'in my opinion young X here... is just about the least mixed up child I have ever examined'. 'Hooray for X,' yelled one of the children. The Other Children clapped and cheered. 'Sssh' said the principal, but no one did.

Later that day X's friends put on their overalls and went to see X. They found X in the yard playing with a very tiny baby that none of them had seen before. The baby was wearing very tiny red and white overalls. 'How do you like our new baby?' X asked the Other Children proudly.

'It's got cute dimples,' said Jim.

'It's got strong muscles too,' said Susie.

'What kind of baby is it?' asked Joe and Peggy.

X frowned at them 'Can't you tell?' Then X broke out into a big mischievous smile. 'It's a Y!!'

Activities

Additional support for teaching these book activities can be found on the Harcourt website at: www.harcourt.co.uk/literature

The additional support resources contain:

- A full scheme of work: 15 short-term lesson plans
- Student Sheets, Teacher's Notes and OHTs to accompany the lesson plans

Kids and Parents

Dear Mum, Please Don't Panic by Allan Frewin Jones

1   **In pairs**, tell each other about a time when you
    accidentally caused damage at home. Talk about:

    • how the accident happened
    • what you did to try to put it right or explain it away
    • whether you were punished – and, if so, how.

2   a **In groups,** trace Jack's sequence of accidents. Copy
       and complete the chart below to show how things go
       from bad to worse.

Jack's accidents		
1 Goes into mum's bedroom for talcum powder – spills it all over the carpet.	2	3
4	5	6

    b Imagine mum returns soon after Jack has left and
       looks round the house. In how many different rooms
       will she find damage? Talk about what you think will
       upset her most, and why.

3   **As a class,** examine how Jack tries to soften the blow for
    mum by the way he writes his letter.

Select four quotations. Then explain them by completing individual copies of the comment chart below.

Comment Chart	
Quotation	**Comment**
'And I'm not wearing my brand new trainers to the party – like you said I shouldn't'	Jack wants to show he's not totally disobedient: he takes *some* notice of mum

4 **In pairs,** act out a conversation between Jack and mum when they next meet. Jack tries to make light of the damage and get into mum's good books, as in the letter. Will it work?

One Christmas Eve by Langston Hughes

This story is set in the USA during the 1950s. There was widespread inequality between white and black Americans.

5 a **In groups**, complete individual copies of the chart below. One entry has been made for you. Use details from the story to make at least three more.

Evidence of the unequal treatment of black people
• Joe's mother, Arcie, works for a well-off white family as their 'maid'. She is paid very little: 'she got only seven dollars a week'.

  b **As a class**, compare your findings. Then make a written summary of what the story shows about racial discrimination.

6 a In pairs, copy and complete the spidergram below. It records Joe's feelings at different points.

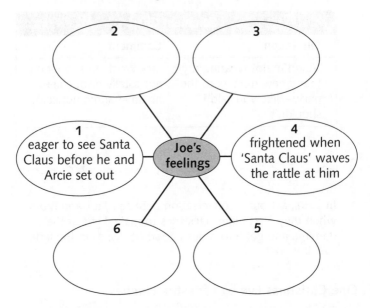

1
eager to see Santa Claus before he and Arcie set out

Joe's feelings

4
frightened when 'Santa Claus' waves the rattle at him

b As a class, use your completed spidergrams to discuss why we feel more and more sorry for Joe as the story goes on. Then write class notes explaining how the author directs our feelings to the five-year-old boy.

Your own writing

7 Write a real or imagined story on **one** of these titles:

• Describe a young person getting into trouble with one or both of their parents. Plan out your story in episodes, and have a clear idea of the ending before you start to write.

• Describe a young person being treated as different or inferior by others. Base your story on the young person's feelings and make your plan accordingly.

Tough Teachers

Excuses, Excuses by Andrew Matthews

1 **As a class**, talk about excuses you have made yourself, or heard others make, for not doing school work on time. Your teacher may join in by recalling some excuses s/he has been given.

Then vote as a class for those which are:

- the most convincing
- the most imaginative
- the most ridiculous.

Explain your choices.

2 At the start of this story, we read: 'Two Red noticed that there was a battle going on. The battle was between Gerry Atkins and Mr Haggerty'.

In pairs, think of this 'battle' as a five-round boxing match. Look over the whole story, then copy and complete the battle chart below.

Battle Chart: Gerry versus Mr Haggerty			
Round	Gerry's tactics	Mr Haggerty's tactics	Winner
1	He claims absence through illness when the work was set	He gives a double homework for Gerry to catch up	?
2			

As a class, compare your completed battle charts. Say with reasons:

- who won the last round
- who was the overall winner
- who was the more skilful opponent.

3 a As a class, scan the story to find whereabouts the following speech verbs come:

squeaked	roared	rasped	seethed
snapped	sneered	beamed	boomed

Discuss what each verb shows about the mood of the speaker. Which do you find the most descriptive?

b By yourself, write an episode to add to the end of the story. In it, Mr Haggerty asks Wayne for the £2 he has won by betting that Gerry will 'get away with it'. Include several speech verbs of your own. Do not use 'said', 'asked', 'answered' or 'replied'.

Father's Help by R.K. Narayan

This story is set in an Indian secondary school in the mid-20th century.

4 a In groups, discuss what the story shows about the differences between an Indian school then and a British school now. Consider:

- the subjects being taught
- discipline
- student–teacher relationships.

b Then complete individual copies of the comparison chart below. Make up to four more entries.

School in India (then)	School in Britain (now)
• pupils have to stand when answering a teacher's question	• question-and-answer in class is less formal
•	•

c As a class, give your views about how students in India were taught. Do you think they would:

- learn well
- behave well
- respect their teachers
- enjoy school?

How good a teacher would Mr Samuel be in a British school today?

5   By the end of this story, Swami is on bad terms with Mr Samuel. He also has a conscience about telling his father that Mr Samuel is violent. This could get the teacher sacked.

By yourself, imagine you are Swami. Plan and write a private letter to Mr Samuel telling him the whole truth about the day described in the story. In this letter:

- give the real reason why you were late for class
- explain your strange behaviour during lessons
- say why you did not hand in your father's letter.

Write about two pages. Use a formal style.

Comparing the two stories

6   This activity asks you to think about the endings of the stories.

As a class, give examples of any short stories or novels you have read that end with a 'twist'. Then fill in an enlarged version of the chart below. Everyone should offer ideas and opinions.

Story	What is the twist at the end of the story?	Why do you think the writer decides to end with a twist?	Do you think it gives the story a good ending?
Excuses, Excuses			
Father's Help			

Home and Away

Kid in a Bin by Robert Carter

1   A rubbish bin in McDonald's is a strange place for a
    runaway child to choose to live. But this is where
    eight-year-old Anthony goes.

   a **In groups**, build up a picture of how Anthony spends a
      typical day and night. Complete individual copies of
      the survival chart below to show how he lives.

Anthony's 24-hour Survival Chart	
Eating	
Sleeping	
Washing and Toilet	
Entertainment	
Friends	
Avoiding discovery	

   b **As a class**, compare your survival charts. Then talk
      about:

   • the reason why Anthony has left home – and why
     he intends to stay way

   • how Robert Carter makes living in a bin seem
     perfectly normal by the way he writes the story.

2   Imagine that at some time in the future Anthony is
    discovered. The local newspaper decides to print his story
    on its front page.

a **As a class**, look at a selection of front page newspaper stories. Talk about:

- *Headlines*: how do they make a strong impact on the reader?
- *First paragraphs*: what kind of information do they give?
- *Interviews*: how do they add detail and human interest to the story?
- *Language*: how does the choice of language make the story sound dramatic?

b **By yourself**, write the front page story about Anthony. Begin by describing how he was found. When planning the rest, think about:

- what 'slant' will you put on it: humorous? serious? weird?
- apart from Anthony, who will you interview: his father? his sister? the McDonald's night manager?
- what will you make your readers feel about Anthony running away from home: naughty? irresponsible? understandable?

Death and the Boy retold by Anthony Horowitz

This story is an adaptation of a folk tale told throughout West Africa. It exists in numerous versions.

3 a **As a class**, talk about:

- what you understand by the terms 'folk tale' and 'fairy story'
- any British folk tales you have read or heard
- why so many ancient folk tales survive to the present day.

b Then make brief notes to show how 'Death and the Boy' is a typical folk tale.

4   A publisher has given you the job of retelling this story
    for a new book of *Traditional Tales* aimed at children
    aged 7–8. You have been sent a Brief: instructions from
    the publisher about how the story should be written and
    presented.

    a **In pairs**, read the publisher's Brief below.

Brief for a new version of 'Death and the Boy'

Target group: Children aged 7–8

Number of pages: 6 pages of A4 size

Layout of each page: Approx 50 words of writing
                        1 coloured illustration

Language and style: Vocabulary suited to ages 7–8
                        Varied sentence structures
                        Mixture of description and speech

Story title: Create a new title if you wish

Overall effect: Exciting! Fast-moving!

    Plan the six-page story. You need to decide:

    • how best to divide the story into episodes, one for
      each page
    • what the main details are that you must keep in
    • which details you can miss out without losing the
      thread
    • how to create suitable illustrations.

    b **By yourself**, write and illustrate the story in its final
    form. Use a computer if you wish.

Comparing the two stories

5   Both stories contain a moral or message. **As a class**, talk
    about the moral you find in each story. Justify your ideas.
    'Death and the Boy' is a very old story; 'Kid in a Bin' is a
    recent one. Do morals change with time?

Tall Stories

The Old Woman Who Lived in a Cola Can
by Bernard Ashley

In the course of this story, the old woman moves house five times.

1   a   **In pairs**, track her moves by copying and completing the flow diagram below.

Old Woman's Home	Old Woman's complaints about it
Cola can	Too small – too shabby – too cold in winter, too hot in summer
↓	↓

   b   **As a class**, use your completed flow diagrams to talk about:

   • why the old woman is never satisfied
   • why you think the author ends the story by having her live back where she started.

2   **In groups**, examine the role of the 'flash young man' in the story. Talk about and make notes on:

   • why he starts helping the old woman and keeps on doing so
   • how he is made to seem a likeable, attractive character
   • how he is shown to have gone up in the world each time he appears
   • how he resembles the fairy godmother figure in pantomime and fairy stories.

3 a As a class, discuss the kind of story known as a fable. Describe any fables you have read, perhaps when you were younger. Then complete individual copies of the chart below.

Typical features of a Fable	
Kinds of plot	
Kinds of character	
Kinds of ending	
Purposes of a fable	

b By yourself, use your chart to write about what 'The Old Woman Who Lived in a Cola Can' has in common with fables. If you think of the story as a modern fable, what moral or message does it have?

Sharlo's Strange Bargain by Ralph Prince

This story is set on the Caribbean island of Antigua. Caribbean countries have a strong tradition of sorcery, or 'obeah', which often features in their folk tales. This is a modern version of one of them.

4 a In groups, complete individual copies of the chart below. One entry has already been made. Make at least three more. Add quotations to prove your points from the text.

Sharlo: how his bargain changes him
• He becomes lazy and stops working altogether: 'But from that same time he stopped cultivating his mountain lands or doing any other work' (page 52).

b **As a class**, use your completed charts to discuss:

- what examples are there of Sharlo becoming a less likeable person than before his bargain?
- why does Sharlo's magic calabash make him an unpopular outsider in his own village?

5 Ralph Prince, the Antiguan author of this story, says it has 'a distinct West Indian flavour'.

In pairs, list at least three features of 'Sharlo's Strange Bargain' that are strongly West Indian. Then combine with another pair and compare your ideas.

6 The 'tall red man' turns out to be the devil. At the end of the story, the devil comes for Sharlo because he has broken his promise to keep their secret.

By yourself, imagine what happens to Sharlo the night after he tells the secret to Zakky. Write this as a horror story. Make your descriptions as vivid and frightening as possible.

Comparing the two stories

7 a **As a class**, talk about and make notes on the similarities between these two fables. Focus on:

- the fates of the old woman and Sharlo
- the characters of 'the flash young man' and 'the tall red man': do they have things in common?
- the morals of the stories: how far are they alike?

b **By yourself**, use your notes to write a comparison of these stories as fables. Produce three or four paragraphs. Quote from the text to back up what you say.

Big Bullies

The Ghost Train by Sydney J. Bounds

1   **In pairs**, read aloud the opening paragraphs of this story.
    A reads from the start to 'Enjoy all the fun of the fair!'.
    B reads on as far as 'the best night of the year until…'
    Then talk about:

    • how the author uses precise description of sights,
      sounds and smells to give a vivid impression of the fair
    • the most exciting experiences *you* have had at
      fairgrounds and/or theme parks. Describe these in
      detail: make your partner feel s/he was there.

2   a   **As a class,** reread the paragraphs where Billy is on the
        Ghost Train trying to escape the bullies. Read from
        'Dim blue lights spelled out GHOST TRAIN' (page 59)
        as far as 'Ed and Higgy scrambled back to the last
        carriage' (page 60).

        Find whereabouts the writer uses the verbs listed in
        Column 1 below. Compare each of them with the
        'possible alternative' in Column 2. Talk about why the
        writer's choice is a better description in the context
        where it appears.

    b   **By yourself,** copy the table and make comments in
        Column 3.

Writer's choice of verb	Possible alternative	Your comments on the writer's choice
rumbled stalked clanked swooped cackled gaped	rushed glided rattled descended roared yawned	

c **As a class**, talk about why verbs can be as powerful as adjectives or adverbs in conveying sights and sounds. Refer to examples in the story.

d **By yourself**, write a three-paragraph description of a visit to a fairground or theme park. Choose your language precisely, especially verbs.

Polyphemus the Cyclops retold by Barbara Leonie Picard

This story is a modern retelling of an ancient Greek myth. The original story was written by Homer in *The Odyssey* three thousand years ago.

3 **By yourself,** use reference books and the internet to find information about Greek myths. Your task is to produce a booklet for people of your age entitled 'A Modern Reader's Guide to Greek Myths'.

Use the information below to research and plan your booklet. Each heading will introduce a double-page spread.

The Greek Gods

- What did the ancient Greeks believe about their gods?
- Who were Zeus, Poseidon and Hades?
- What powers did they have? Give examples.

The Greek Heroes

- Who were the 'heroes'?
- What connection did they have with the gods?
- Why did Odysseus become the most famous 'hero' of all?

The Odyssey

- What series of linked stories does *The Odyssey* tell?
- Briefly outline the stories of **i** the Sirens **ii** Calypso.

In your finished booklet, combine illustrations with writing to inform and explain. Produce it on a computer and show it to others in your class.

4   a   **In pairs**, reread the part of this story where Odysseus and his men get Polyphemus drunk on wine and put out his eye. Read from 'When evening came the Cyclops returned…' (page 66) to ' …crouched trembling against the wall' (page 67).

What would you see on screen if this passage were filmed? Concentrate on close ups: the inside of the cave; what Polyphemus's face looks like; how he moves about after having drunk too much wine; his eye being put out; how he tries to catch Odysseus after being blinded.

b   **By yourself**, write your own version of this passage. Make the description vivid by concentrating on small visual details.

Comparing the two stories

5   In stories about big bullies, most readers enjoy seeing them get their just desserts.

As a class, compare the ways in which Ed, Higgy and Polyphemus end up being beaten. Consider: **i** how each writer shows this happening and **ii** in which story you find the bullies' defeat more effective, and why.

Gangs and Dares

Chicken by Mary Hoffman

1   Look at the list of 'Reasons why teenagers form or join
    gangs' below. They were put forward by a class of 13-
    year-olds.

    a **In groups,** discuss how far you agree with them. Show
      what you think by giving each Reason a mark out of
      5, where 1 = Don't Agree, 3 = Agree Up to a Point,
      and 5 = Agree Strongly.

Reasons why teenagers form or join gangs	Mark out of 5
• So as not to be left out of the 'in crowd'	
• To prove to yourself and others you are tough	
• To give yourself a bigger identity than you can have with just a best friend	
• To protect yourself against bullies	
• Because it is human nature to go round in groups	

    b **As a class**, i add to the list any other Reasons you
      think should be on it and ii discuss whether boys and
      girls have different attitudes to being in gangs.

2   **In pairs,** imagine you belong to the Inliners gang
    described in this story. You keep a diary of all the dares
    you do. Each entry has three headings:

    A Particular dare done
    B Reasons for doing it
    C How successful it was and why.

    Choose **two** of the Inliners' dares from different parts of
    the story. Make notes on them, then each write up one
    of the diary entries in full.

Poinsettias by Beverley Naidoo

This story is set in the Cape Province region of South Africa, a mainly rural area with large farms. It was written in 1995.

3 By yourself, read the details below. They will help you appreciate the story more fully.

> • In 1994, Nelson Mandela was elected South Africa's first black President. Apartheid, the previous government's policy of segregating black people and white people, was expected to be ended.
>
> • Many white South Africans are descended from Dutch settlers. As well as English, they speak their own language: Afrikaans. In the story, Jan Venter is one of these Afrikaaners. He owns a large orange plantation and employs black labourers and servants who live separately from the white people.
>
> • Veronica's white family live in Johannesburg. There they employ a black maid, Rebecca. In the story, they are staying on holiday with an Afrikaans family, the van Reenans, who own the neighbouring farm to Jan Venter's.

4 As a class, talk about and make notes on: **i** the differences between the way black people and white people lived at that time in South Africa, and **ii** the way white people treat black people in this story. Consider:

- the description of Rebecca's room (page 83) compared with the van Reenan's farmhouse (page 81)
- the description of the 'workers' compound' on Jan Venter's farm (page 87)
- the difference between the way Jan Venter treats the black boy and the way he treats Veronica (pages 89–90).

Then summarise what Beverley Naidoo shows us about racism in South Africa when she wrote the story.

5 **By yourself**, imagine you are Veronica. On the day after the events described in the story, you write a confidential letter to Rebecca, your family's black maid in Johannesburg.

The letter describes what happened when you did your dare and how you feel about it as you look back now. Prepare for this by checking in the story:

- why Veronica goes ahead with the dare, despite her anxieties about it
- what she thinks when she sees Jan Venter beating the black boy who 'looked like Selo, Rebecca's son' (page 89)
- why she feels a mixture of relief and guilt at the end of the story.

Write Veronica's letter in the first person. Use a direct and personal style.

6 **As a class**, reread carefully **i** the first twenty lines of this story and **ii** the final paragraph.

Talk about what is meant by *symbolism* in a piece of writing. Then discuss why these two passages can be seen as symbolic in the light of the story as a whole.

Your own writing

7 At the end of 'Chicken', we read 'The local papers tried to turn Alfie into a hero'.

By yourself, imagine you are a local journalist. Write a front page story about the accident at Silbury Cuttings with the headline *Schoolboys in Railway Line Drama*. Produce it on a computer.

Best of Enemies

The New Boy by Geddes Thomson

1 a **In pairs**, exchange memories of a time when you felt like an outsider or a stranger. It may have been when you joined a new school, class, club, team or other group. It may have been when you moved house, when you were on holiday, when you got lost in a strange place, etc.

   b **By yourself**, write a page about the time you have been remembering.

   c **As a class**, listen to some of these accounts read aloud by their writers. Then talk about:

   • how it feels to be 'new'
   • how newcomers get treated
   • at what point, and for what reasons, newcomers become accepted.

2 a **In groups**, trace the relationship between Tam and Colin in this story. Complete individual copies of the flow diagram below to show how they start out as enemies and end up as friends. Make four more entries.

Relationship between Tam and Colin		
What Tam does	**How Colin reacts**	**Consequence**
Mocks Colin's accent (pages 91 and 92)	Goes quiet and won't rise to the bait (page 92)	Tam thinks he's put Colin down (page 92)
↓	↓	↓
Shows off in the English lesson (page 93)	Gives a much better answer than Tam (page 93)	Tam is hurt and decides to 'sort out the new boy' (page 94)

  b As a class, use your completed diagrams to discuss:

- why Tam is aggressive towards Colin at first
- which of the two boys is chiefly responsible for them becoming friends
- how true to life you find this account of a relationship between teenagers.

3 By yourself, write in role as Tam an account of his first day at the school. Bring out:

- his personality as it is presented in the story
- his impressions of the pupils and teachers in general
- his thoughts and feelings about himself and Tam.

The Fight by Ruskin Bond

This story is set in present-day India. When they first meet, Vijay thinks himself superior to Anil because of his background.

4 As a class, discuss whether people in some parts of Britain look down on others because of:

- where they live
- their education
- how they speak
- the jobs they do.

Do you think there is regional or class prejudice in Britain today? Give your reasons.

5 a In groups, consider which of the two boys Ruskin Bond wants you to feel more sympathy for. Show what you think by completing individual copies of the chart overleaf. One entry has already been made. Make up to four more.

Which character does the author want you to have more sympathy for?	
Anil	Vijay
• Finds the pool and thinks of it as his alone: 'he lay naked on a rock' (page 99)	• Challenges Anil for the 'ownership' of the pool: 'This is my pool. I did not invite you to it' (page 99)

b **As a class,** refer to your completed charts to discuss the questions below.

• Which of the boys turns out to be the stronger, and which the weaker, character?
• The story ends with Anil 'smiling that he had won the day'. Do you think Anil has won the day? Give your reasons.
• This is a story about rivalry between people from different parts of the same country. What explanations does the story give for this rivalry?
• Towards the end of the story, Vijay says to Anil 'We are friends now, yes?' (page 104). Do you think they ever really can be? Give your reasons.

Comparing the two stories

6 **By yourself,** write on the following topic:

Compare the relationships described in these two stories – the first between Tam and Colin, the second between Anil and Vijay.

What similarities and what differences do you find between them? Back up your ideas with quotations.

Caught in Between

On the Bench by Stephen Potts

1   a   **In pairs**, work out from Gary's letters, phone calls and
        e-mails what happens between his father and mother
        in this story.

    Make notes to show what you find, like this:

    > • At the start, dad is away in the army (Letter 1)
    >
    > • When he comes home on leave at Christmas, his dad
    >   and mum argue a lot (Letter 2)

    Continue in this way to the end. Sometimes you will
    need to read between the lines. Where the facts are
    uncertain, give your joint opinion about what is
    happening in Gary's parents' lives.

    b   **Combine with another pair**. Compare your ideas. Then
        talk about the story's ending, in particular:

    • are Mam and Dad now living completely separate
      lives?
    • how is Mam's mood different from earlier in the
      story? How do you account for this?

2   a   **As a class**, discuss and make notes on **i** the way
        Stephen Potts chooses to tell this story and **ii** how the
        story's structure and style affects the reader's response.

    Consider:

    • What is achieved by telling the story in the first
      person?
    • What is the effect of using a sequence of letters from
      Gary to Dad (as opposed, say, to entries in his diary)?
    • This is an unusual story in that we never hear the
      writer's own voice. What do you think are the
      advantages or disadvantages of this?

b **By yourself**, use your notes to write on the following topic:

Describe Stephen Potts's narrative technique in 'On the Bench'. What are its main effects on you as a reader?

She by Rosa Guy

This story is set in modern-day North America. The narrator, Gogi, her father Harry and her sister Linda are from the West Indies. Gogi's West Indian mother has died and Harry is remarried to Dorine.

3 **As a class**, quote examples from the story of Dorine's hostile attitude to Gogi. Complete individual copies of the chart below to show what you find. Make three more entries.

Dorine's attitude to Gogi	
Quotation	**Point**
• 'No, you're not,' [going to the bathroom] she said. 'Not before you wash up these dishes.' (page 112)	She picks on Gogi unfairly
• 'This girl's just too damn lazy…' (page 112)	She complains loudly about Gogi – criticising her

Give your ideas about why 'Daddy let her get away with everything' (page 115). What light does this throw on his character?

4   a   **As a class**, share your knowledge of the story of *Cinderella*. Make brief notes about its story and characters.

    b   **In groups**, remind yourself of the last sentence of 'She'. Use this as a starting-point for considering the story as a modern version of 'Cinderella'. Gogi could be seen as Cinderella; Dorine could be seen as the wicked stepmother.

      Make up to four more entries on an individual copy of the chart below.

Similarities and differences between 'Cinderella' and 'She'	
• Cinderella has a stepmother who treats her cruelly	• Dorine becomes Gogi's stepmother and is nasty and spiteful towards her

    c   **As a class,** consider why there are more differences than similarities. What point do you think Rosa Guy is making by bringing this out?

Comparing the two stories

5   **By yourself**, write about:

- how each story's title relates to its plot, characters and themes
- which title you think is more appropriate to its story.

Produce two to three pages. Use quotations to back up the points you make.

Young and Old

Who's Afraid? by Philippa Pearce

1   It has been said that teenagers often get on better with
    their grandparents, and older people generally, than they
    do with other adults.

    In pairs, talk about relationships *you* have, or have had,
    with the 'older generation'. Is the above comment true in
    your case? Why do you think young and old people
    often understand each other so well?

2   **In groups,** talk about the impressions of Great-
    grandmother you get from this story. Copy and complete
    the grid below to show what you decide. Make at least
    two more entries.

Impressions of Great-grandmother	
Point	**Textual reference**
1 Physically very frail	• 'she had become blind in old age. Whether she heard much was doubtful' • 'For a second he felt her weakly pull away'

    Use your completed grids to consider Great-grandmother's
    character. Is there more to her than her age and illness?

3   **As a class,** look at the story's final sentence: 'Joe said
    nothing; but he wished now that he had kissed her
    cheek, to say goodbye, and to thank her'.

Use this as a starting-point to discuss why Joe should feel grateful to Great-grandmother. Focus on:

- Joe's fear of Dicky Hutt
- how Great-grandmother protects Joe
- the comment by Joe's father, 'When I was a little boy, she was fun. I remember her. Jokey, then: full of tricks…' (page 124).

A Game of Cards by Witi Ihimaera

This story is set in a Maori community in New Zealand. The Maoris were the original inhabitants of New Zealand with their own language and customs. They are now a part of its multicultural society.

4 **In groups**, complete individual copies of the character-gram below for Nanny Miro. Include quotations.

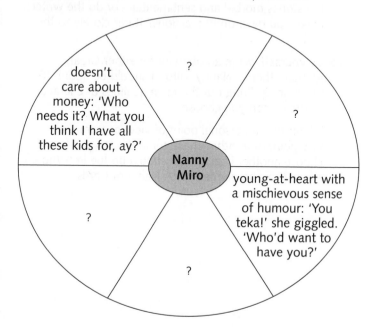

As a class, use your completed character-grams to examine **i** how Witi Ihimaera presents Nanny Miro to the reader and **ii** what impressions of her he wants us to take away from this story. Talk about:

- the effect of having us see her through the eyes of her grown-up nephew who has known her all his life
- the fact that many of the impressions given of her are humorous ones (find examples)
- the reactions we are made to have to her death.

Comparing the two stories

5 a **As a class,** compare the way Philippa Pearce presents Great-grandmother with the way Witi Ihimaera presents Nanny Miro.

   Both of them are near to death. Do you find either of the stories morbid and sentimental – or do the writers make you have other reactions? Refer closely to the text.

   b **By yourself**, write an obituary for either Great-grandmother or Nanny Miro. It should be about 200 words long. Bring out the main qualities of character of the person you choose.

   Write from a personal point of view **or** from the viewpoint of another character in the story. If you choose another character, it should be Joe in 'Who's Afraid?' or the nephew in 'A Game of Cards'.

Odd One Out

Baby X by Anon

This contemporary story is from North America. It explores gender roles and relationships in western society.

1 **In pairs**, Partner **A** acts a male and Partner **B** a female in the scenarios below. Role-play one of them by improvising or by using a prepared script.

   • **A** and **B** are part of a teenage group who go around together. They are in town one Saturday. They have conflicting ideas about how to spend the afternoon. Act out their argument.

   • **A** and **B** are members of your school's Year Social Committee. They are meeting to plan an end-of-year celebration for the whole Year, which is roughly 50% boys and 50% girls. They come up with totally different suggestions. Act out their disagreement.

   • **A** and **B** are on your School Council. The Head has decided to bring in a new uniform policy. A meeting has been called to decide what will be suitable for girls and what for boys. **A** and **B** have differing views. Act out the points they make in the meeting.

2 **As a class**, discuss what is meant by 'gender stereotyping'. Then put forward your views about:

   • Magazines aimed at teenage boys and teenage girls: how do they appeal to their respective audiences?

   • Careers advice given in your school to the two sexes: is it differentiated by gender?

   • Birthday cards you got when you were younger: are there boys' cards and girls' cards – and, if so, what messages do they give those who receive them?

Then hold a formal debate on the motion: 'This class believes discrimination between males and females in our society is a thing of the past.'

3 a In groups, complete individual copies of the chart below. It records examples of gender stereotyping in 'Baby X'. Two entries have already been made. Find at least four more.

Examples of gender stereotyping in 'Baby X'	
Incident/Comment	**What this shows**
• When Mr Jones goes shopping, he finds that baby clothes and toys are separated into 'Boys' and 'Girls'	Manufacturers encourage parents to treat their male and female children differently from birth
• 'Now, Tracy... little girls mustn't hit little ...' (page 134)	Adults teach young children how to behave in line with gender expectation

b As a class, use your completed charts to discuss:

- how does Baby X, as it grows older, reverse the gender stereotyping described on your charts?

- what is the effect on 'Other Children' of X not behaving as either a typical boy or a typical girl?

4 By yourself, write a discursive essay on the topic below.

'Baby X' has been called 'a modern satire on the way society makes artificial distinctions between the sexes. It conveys serious points through humour'.

How far do you agree with this comment? Quote from the text to support what you say.

Comparing Baby X with other stories

5 a **As a class**, choose **one** other story from this collection which deals with discrimination and prejudice. Compare it with 'Baby X'. Discuss:

   • what different forms can prejudice take?
   • what point about prejudice is the author making at the end of 'Baby X'?
   • compare this ending with the ending of the other story you are discussing. Do the endings give a similar or a different message?

   b **By yourself**, write a comparison between 'Baby X' and one or more other stories in this collection. What similarities and differences do you find in them?

National Curriculum Objectives Chart

Stories		Main Framework Objectives covered in the Activities		
	Year	Speaking and Listening (S&L)	Text Level – Reading (R)	Text Level – Writing (Wr)
Dear Mum, Please Don't Panic (page 1)	Year 7	S&L 1, 2, 15, 16	R 2, 7, 8, 9	Wr 1, 2, 5, 6
One Christmas Eve (page 5)	Year 8	S&L 2, 7, 13, 14	R 3, 4, 5, 10	Wr 1, 3, 5, 6
	Year 9	S&L 1, 2, 11, 12	R 1, 3, 6, 11	Wr 1, 2, 5, 15
Excuses, Excuses (page 11)	Year 7	S&L2, 5, 12, 13	R 2, 6, 14, 15	Wr 1, 2, 8, 10
Father's Help (page 18)	Year 8	S&L 2, 5, 10, 12	R 4, 5, 7, 10	Wr 2, 3, 7, 10
	Year 9	S&L 2, 5, 8, 10	R 1, 3, 11, 12	Wr 1, 2, 6, 10
Kid in a Bin (page 26)	Year 7	S&L 1, 5, 10, 12	R 2, 6, 7, 12	Wr 5, 7, 10, 11
Death and the Boy (page 35)	Year 8	S&L 5, 7, 10, 11	R 3, 4, 10, 11	Wr 7, 8, 10, 18
	Year 9	S&L 5, 7, 10, 12	R 1, 6, 7, 12	Wr 5, 7, 10, 16
The Old Woman Who Lived in a Cola Can (page 42)	Year 7	S&L 6, 12, 13, 14	R 2, 8, 12, 14	Wr 5, 7, 18, 19
	Year 8	S&L 1, 8, 10, 11	R 4, 5, 11, 16	Wr 6, 8, 11, 17
Sharlo's Strange Bargain (page 48)	Year 9	S&L 7, 8, 9, 10	R 3, 6, 7, 16	Wr 5, 10, 11, 17

	Main Framework Objectives covered in the Activities			
Stories	Year	Speaking and Listening (S&L)	Text Level – Reading (R)	Text Level – Writing (Wr)
The Ghost Train (page 57)	Year 7	S&L 4, 5, 7, 13	R 2, 6, 12, 14	Wr 6, 7, 11, 12
Polyphemus the Cyclops (page 62)	Year 8	S&L 1, 5, 10, 11	R 3, 4, 7, 10	Wr 5, 6, 7, 8
	Year 9	S&L 2, 4, 5, 7	R 2, 6, 11, 12	Wr 4, 6, 9, 11
Chicken (page 70)	Year 7	S&L 5, 13, 15, 17	R 6, 7, 12, 16	Wr 2, 10, 11, 12
Poinsettias (page 80)	Year 8	S&L 10, 11, 14, 16	R 5, 6, 8, 10	Wr 1, 5, 10, 12
	Year 9	S&L 1, 2, 5, 9	R 6, 7, 11, 12	Wr 3, 7, 9, 11
The New Boy (page 91)	Year 7	S&L 5, 8, 13, 14	R 6, 9, 14, 15	Wr 6, 7, 18, 19
The Fight (page 98)	Year 8	S&L 2, 5, 7, 10	R 4, 5, 10, 16	Wr 5, 7, 16, 17
	Year 9	S&L 1, 2, 5, 9	R 3, 6, 7, 11	Wr 5, 6, 16, 17
On the Bench (page 105)	Year 7	S&L 5, 6, 7, 14	R 6, 8, 12, 14	Wr 15, 16, 18, 19
She (page 112)	Year 8	S&L 7, 9, 10, 11	R 7, 10, 11, 16	Wr 13, 14, 16, 17
	Year 9	S&L 5, 7, 9, 10	R 6, 7, 10, 11	Wr 2, 13, 16, 17

Main Framework Objectives covered in the Activities				
Stories	Year	Speaking and Listening (S&L)	Text Level – Reading (R)	Text Level – Writing (Wr)
Who's Afraid? (page 119)	Year 7	S&L 2, 4, 5, 10	R 8, 12, 14, 16	Wr 10, 11, 18, 19
A Game of Cards (page 125)	Year 8	S&L 2, 7, 5, 10	R 3, 7, 10, 11	Wr 5, 10, 16, 17
	Year 9	S&L 1, 2, 5, 8	R 5, 6, 7, 12	Wr 9, 10, 16, 17
Baby X (page 132)	Year 7	S&L 2, 5, 11, 15	R 6, 8, 12, 16	Wr 15, 16, 18, 19
	Year 8	S&L 5, 7, 12, 14	R 4, 7, 10, 16	Wr 13, 14, 16, 17
	Year 9	S&L 5, 8, 9, 12	R 1, 6, 7, 12	Wr 13, 14, 16, 17

Whale Rider

Witi Ihimaera

A magical and mythical story...

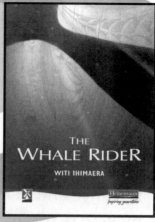

978 0 435131 081
Age 11+   Hardback 144pp

Kahu craves her grandfather's attention; but he is
busy as chief of a Maori tribe that claims descent from
the legendary Whale Rider. Every generation, a male
has inherited the title of chief, but now there is no
male heir. There is only Kahu. She should be next in
line, but her great grandfather is blinded by tradition.
Kahu, however, has a unique gift – the ability to
communicate with the whales.

Tel: 01865 888080   **Fax:**   01865 314091
Email: enquiries@harcourt.co.uk   **Web:** www.harcourt.co.uk

M197

From Harcourt

The Other Side of Truth

Beverley Naidoo

A compelling, sensitive and moving read.

978 0 435125 30 1
Age 12+   Hardback 216pp

'A shot. Two shots at the gate in the early morning and a car screeches away down an avenue of palm trees.'

When their mother is killed in a shooting, twelve-year-old Sade and her younger brother Femi – children of an outspoken Nigerian journalist – are forced to flee for their lives. They are smuggled out of Nigeria and sent to London where their uncle lives. But when they get to London, they find themselves abandoned and alone.

This is a thought-provoking read that tackles themes of injustice, the right to freedom of speech and the complexities of political asylum.

Tel: 01865 888080   **Fax:** 01865 314091
Email: enquiries@harcourt.co.uk   **Web:** www.harcourt.co.uk

From Harcourt

Tell the Moon to Come Out

Joan Lingard

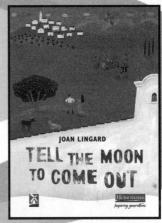

978 0 435131 04 3

Age 11+   Hardback 192pp

The Spanish Civil War has left the country shattered.
Nick's father went to fight for the Republican cause,
but has not returned. Undeterred, Nick sets off to
search for him, crossing illegally into Spain and hiding
from the authorities. He meets Isabel, the daughter of
a cruel Civil Guard. This could be Nick's only chance to
find the truth about his father – but can he trust her?

Tel: 01865 888080
Email: enquiries@harcourt.co.uk

Fax: 01865 314091
Web: www.harcourt.co.uk

M197

From Harcourt

Across the Nightingale Floor

Lian Hearn

Love, violence and revenge in one stunning read...

978 0 435120 28 3
Age 13+   Hardback 272pp

Sixteen-year-old Takeo returns from a solitary journey over the mountain to find his village aflame, bodies littering the ground, including those of his parents. Takeo is rescued by Otori Shigeru, the lord of a neighbouring clan. Muted by the need for revenge, Takeo is tutored in the ancient ways of Otori martial culture, to fight one last battle with the clan who destroyed his family.

The author's lifelong interest in Japan led to the writing of this thrilling tale.

Tel: 01865 888080   **Fax:**   01865 314091
Email: enquiries@harcourt.co.uk   **Web:** www.harcourt.co.uk

M197

From Harcourt

The best in classic and

Jane Austen

Elizabeth Laird

Beverley Naidoo   Roddy Doyle

Robert Swindells

George Orwell

Charles Dickens

Charlotte Brontë

Jan Mark

Anne Fine

Anthony Horowitz